EARTH SATELLITES

Also by Patrick Moore

GUIDE TO THE MOON
GUIDE TO THE PLANETS
THE STORY OF MAN AND THE STARS

with H. Percy Wilkins

HOW TO MAKE AND USE A TELESCOPE

Also by Irving Geis, with Darrell Huff

HOW TO LIE WITH STATISTICS

Earth Satellites

By PATRICK MOORE, F.R.A.S.

Director of the Mercury and Venus Section of the
British Astronomical Association and Fellow and
Council Member of the British Interplanetary Society

Illustrated by IRVING GEIS

New York

W · W · NORTON & COMPANY · INC ·

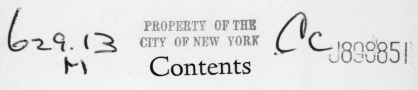

Contents

Foreword

ONLY A few years ago, the idea of setting up artificial moons to circle the Earth would have sounded fantastic. Now that the launching of such bodies is definitely to take place, the subject has come very much into the public eye. Everyone is asking such questions as: How will the satellites be set up? What will they contain? What will they look like, and what use will they be?

Plenty of technical information is available, but the non-specialist reader often finds that he is out of his depth. What I have tried to do in the present book is to give a general picture of what is going on so that after reading what I have written the interested onlooker will find it easier to understand more technical expositions. If I succeed in helping anyone in this way, I shall be more than content. I must of course add that the views advanced here with regard to interplanetary prospects are entirely my own, and are not necessarily those of any particular society or association, so that I alone must be held responsible for them.

I would like to give my particular thanks to Mr. Irving Geis. Mr. Geis has provided all the illustrations, but he has done far more than that; he has made invaluable suggestions, he has gathered information, and he has been of great help in every way. One could not wish for a better collaborator. I am also grateful for the help afforded by the publishers, and in particular by Mr. Eric Swenson.

PATRICK MOORE

East Grinstead, Sussex.
1956
June 12.

Illustrator's Note

ALL of the drawings in this book are based on documentary evidence of some sort. For example, the pictorial descriptions of Russian rockets on page 15 are the very latest available. (1881 and 1903) But the most interesting documentation came to me from a prominent New York bookdealer who is also a space enthusiast. I was trying to find pictorial concepts of men from other planets. The following telephone conversation took place:

Me: "Could you tell me, sir, what you think a Martian looks like?"
Space Enthusiast: "What do *you* think they look like?"
Me: "I haven't the faintest notion."
Space Enthusiast: "They look just like you and me."

I know what *I* look like, and I don't look like a Martian; so a Martian must look like a New York bookdealer. There are other schools of thought on this subject—see pictures on pages 142–143.

The more down-to-earth space scientists were extremely co-operative, particularly those scientists at the Naval Research Laboratory responsible for launching the first actual satellite. I would like especially to thank Drs. Newell, Tousey, Friedman, and particularly Milton Rosen for giving me information on the Vanguard satellite vehicle. I am indebted to Dr. Fred Singer for telling me about the MOUSE; to Willy Ley for being so generous with his rare German space documents; to Lloyd Mallan for the most recent information on men, rockets, space rats and space monkeys; to Hugo Gernsback for contributing valuable photostatic documents; to Martha Demaras of the Museum of Natural History for her help in finding pictures; to Howard Schneider for helping on the "deluxe" space station on pages 104 and 105; and to Fred Freeman for generously consenting to our lampoon of his magnificent painting.

In spite of my sometimes lighthearted approach, all of the scientific institutions were without exception co-operative and helpful. To name only a few: The Smithsonian Institution, the Institute of Aeronautical Sciences, the Hayden Planetarium, and the American Rocket Society.

IRVING GEIS

EARTH SATELLITES

Jet-propelled space ship for flying to the Sun, proposed in 1656 by Cyrano de Bergerac — poet, swordsman, and science fiction writer. Heated air escaping from top of ship supposedly pulled the ship upward. Actually, the reverse would happen.

CHAPTER 1

The Satellite Program

ON JULY 29, 1955, it was officially announced from the White House that the construction and launching of small unmanned space satellites had been approved by the United States Government, and that the first practical experiments were to take place some time between July 1957 and December 1958.

This announcement, the first concrete admission that flight beyond the atmosphere is an immediate possibility, aroused a great deal of interest all over the world. On the following day every national newspaper in Britain devoted its main columns to the subject, under headlines ranging from a sober "Space Satellites to be Launched" to a more speculative "First Step to the Moon!" It was, however, stressed that the first artificial satellites will be used mainly for upper-atmosphere research, and that space travel in the real sense of the word still lies in the distant future.*

The original statement was issued by Dr. Bronk, Presi-

* In June, 1956, a U.S. Defense Department official stated that the U.S. could launch a space satellite carrying eighty men in ten to fifteen years and send a round-trip ship to the moon in twenty to twenty-five years.

dent of the National Academy of Sciences, and Dr. Waterman, Director of the National Science Foundation. The White House press secretary was also present. A general outline of the program was given, coupled with the assurance that information gained from the experiment would be passed on to scientists all over the world—including those on the far side of the Iron Curtain. The press secretary referred to President Eisenhower's "personal gratification that this American program will provide scientists of all nations with an important and unique opportunity for the advancement of science."

Such a statement would have been impossible only a year or so earlier, but needless to say it was most welcome. Immediate reactions from Russia were encouraging. Mr. Khrushchev, Secretary of the Communist Party, said that the Soviet Union would support the project provided that it was "in the interests of humanity," which was in accordance with the emphasis laid by the White House spokesmen upon the nonmilitary aspect of the program.

High-altitude exploration has also been carried on by Russian workers, and shortly after the American announcement two Soviet scientists, Professors Sedov and Ogorodnikov, stated that Russia too was preparing an upper-altitude program. British plans have been rather different, and research has been done more by means of normal rockets than by plans for an orbital vehicle, but this is, of course, merely another way of attacking the same fundamental problems.

The statement by Sedov and Ogorodnikov was issued from Copenhagen, in Denmark, where the sixth congress of the International Astronautical Federation (the I.A.F.) opened on August 1. The I.A.F., a loosely knit body consisting of representatives of all the world's leading Interplanetary Societies, was created in 1949 and had held five previous congresses, but the Copenhagen meeting was the first to be attended by scientists from the Soviet Union.

As its name suggests, the I.A.F. is concerned ultimately

ROCKET POWER, a Russian first.

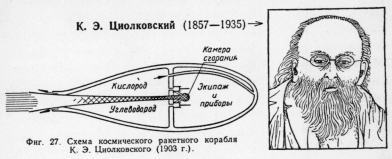

К. Э. Циолковский (1857—1935) →

Камера
сгорания

Кислород

Экипаж
и
приборы

Углеводород

Фиг. 27. Схема космического ракетного корабля
К. Э. Циолковского (1903 г.).

K. E. Ziolkovsky and his 1903 concept of a rocket space ship.

Н. И. Кибальчич
(1853—1881)

N. I. Kibaltchitch and his 1881 design for a "rocket airplane."
Thus the Russians were the first with concept of rocket power.
Documents above are latest available information from Russia.

with the possibilities of space travel. Yet we must be very careful not to jump to conclusions. When the White House announcement became widely known, there were many people only too ready to believe that a trip to the Moon was within sight—and might be accomplished next week, next month or next year. This is far from being the case. At first the satellite program will deal entirely with research into the upper reaches of our own air mantle, and the tiny unmanned bodies will circle the Earth at heights of only a few hundreds of miles, whereas the Moon is almost a quarter of a million miles away.

When an artificial satellite is mentioned, the instinctive question must be: "Even if it can be placed two or three hundred miles above the Earth, why will it not fall down?" The answer is simple enough, but as a good many fundamental principles are involved it is worth considering in some detail.

The Earth, as we know, is an almost spherical body revolving round the Sun at a distance of some 93 million miles. It does not fall into the Sun for the excellent reason that it is moving along in its path or "orbit" at a speed of about 18½ miles a second (66,000 miles per hour). The best everyday analogy, though actually an incorrect one, is to picture a stone being whirled round on the end of a length of cord. So long as the stone is kept moving fast enough to keep the cord stretched, it will not fall, but will continue moving in a circle.

If the whirling motion is stopped, the stone falls almost at once. There are two reasons for this. First, the stone is braked by air resistance; secondly, it is subject to a powerful gravitational pull acting to all intents and purposes in one direction only (downwards). Neither of these limitations apply in space. Above a few hundreds of miles there is almost no air left, so that resistance can be disregarded; and a body moving at the correct speed is in a condition of "free fall." It goes on moving simply because there is nothing to stop it. The force of gravity can be said to act much in the manner of the tightened cord.

We can now see why the Earth does not fall into the Sun; it is safe while it is moving, because "the cord is tight," and there is nothing to check its motion, so that we need have no fear of falling headlong into the solar flames. Similarly, the Moon cannot fall on to the Earth. If we could place an artificial satellite in orbit above the atmosphere, it too would remain circling the Earth indefinitely. The main problem is, of course, how to get it there.

Another important question is: "What is the use of such a satellite?" Here again we can give a straightforward answer. We live at the bottom of an ocean of air, just as a fish lives in an ocean of water, and this air is necessary for our existence. Without it, no life on Earth could have evolved; worlds which are virtually airless, such as the Moon and the planet Mercury, are also virtually lifeless. There are, however, various investigations which cannot be undertaken from ground level. For example, the Sun sends out radiations of all wavelengths. Some of these radiations reach us as visible light, while others can be detected as infrared or ultraviolet light, invisible to the eye but revealed by special instruments and the photographic plate. Yet many of the radiations cannot reach ground level at all, because the atmosphere is opaque to them; they are blocked out, just as a flashlight beam is blocked by a sheet of cardboard. Transferring our instruments to the top of a high mountain will not help much, and if we are to study these radiations we must do so from above the densest part of the atmosphere.

Since 1946 this has been done by sending up rockets fitted with recording instruments, and a great deal of useful information has been gathered. However, a rocket is unsatisfactory in many ways. It remains above the air only for a brief period at the top of its climb, and we want to carry on our observations for hours on end instead of for two or three minutes. Moreover, the subsequent fall of the rocket leads to almost certain destruction of the delicate instruments carried, even though all types of parachute braking have been tried.

If we are to explore the upper air, we must have a vehicle capable of staying "in space" for a lengthy period; in fact, we must have an orbital satellite. Such a plan has been under consideration for many years, but before we consider the satellite itself we must pay some attention to the work accomplished by older methods.

CHAPTER 2

High-Altitude Research

PUTTING an artificial satellite into orbit around the Earth will be an expensive process. It is very hard to give a clear estimate of the cost, but it must be reckoned in many millions of dollars, even if we disregard the money spent upon research over the past half-century. A question that will certainly be asked many times is, therefore: "Is it worth while?"

A few million dollars is very little when compared with the cost of a major war, or for that matter a minor one, and the uses of the satellite will be many. It is not only a question of studying solar radiations and winds in the upper air. Modern weather forecasting, for instance, is decidedly uncertain, and reliable long-range predictions would be of immense value to farmers. We cannot hope to learn all about the atmosphere merely by studying the lower reaches of it; until we are thoroughly familiar with the upper air as well, our knowledge is bound to be patchy.

The atmospheric shell surrounding the Earth is comparatively shallow. The Arab astronomers of nine hundred years ago believed it to be a thousand miles deep, which is not much when compared with the Earth's diameter of 7,926 miles, but this was merely a guess. The first serious investigations became possible in the seventeenth century, when Torricelli, a pupil of the famous Italian scientist Galileo, invented the barometer.

Torricelli realized that the air above us is bound to exert a pressure, and he found this pressure to be some 14.7 lb. to the square inch, enough to balance a column of mercury about 30 inches high. Blaise Pascal, of France, developed the idea by suggesting that pressure must therefore decrease with altitude, and when his brother-in-law Périer took a barometer to the summit of the Puy de Dôme, in Auvergne, it was found that the pressure did indeed fall off as Pascal supposed. Later, in 1714, a general investigation was carried out by Edmund Halley, the second British Astronomer Royal, who is remembered chiefly by the famous comet which bears his name but who made his main contribution to science by persuading Newton to publish the immortal *Principia*. Halley arrived at a total atmospheric depth of 45 miles, and also stated that temperature as well as pressure should decrease with altitude.

Great advances were made during the next hundred and fifty years. The lower air was analyzed, and found to consist of 20.99 per cent by volume of oxygen, 78.03 per cent of nitrogen, 0.94 per cent of argon, and 0.04 per cent of other gases such as neon, helium, krypton, xenon and carbon dioxide, plus a small and variable amount of water vapor. Halley's "lapse rate," or fall in temperature with height, was found to amount to 3 degrees Fahrenheit per thousand feet. The composition of the upper air remained unknown, though in 1804 two French scientists, Gay-Lussac and Biot, went up to 23,000 feet in a balloon and discovered that there was less water vapor at high levels.

The first manned balloons, beginning in 1783 with the

hot-air Montgolfières, were of little help. The very nature of a manned balloon limits it to low levels, and in the closing years of the nineteenth century experiments were made with unmanned balloons equipped with automatic instruments and recording devices. The most important experiments were those of another Frenchman, Teisserenc de Bort, and modern high-altitude research may be said to commence with his work.

Some of Teisserenc de Bort's balloons ascended to dizzy heights of nine or ten miles, and one interesting fact emerged. The lapse rate was not constant. The temperature dropped at a constant rate to —60° Fahrenheit at an altitude of about six miles. Above this altitude variations were not significant. It seemed as though the air were made up of two sharply defined "shells," and Teisserenc de Bort's names for them—"troposphere" for the lower layer and "stratosphere" for the upper —have come into general use, the separating region being known as the "tropopause."

Balloon ascents could not help much further, but some more information was gained from study of sound waves. When an explosion takes place, the noise is often heard by distant observers although inaudible to those closer to the source; there are definite zones of silence. Moreover, there is a marked delay before the sound reaches observers who lie from 60 to 120 miles away. These effects were noticed at the time of the disastrous Krakatoa explosion of 1883, and when "minute guns" were fired at the funeral of Queen Victoria the zones of silence were carefully measured. It seemed unlikely that the upper air could be made up of gases entirely different from those lower down, and the only other explanation was that a high-temperature belt existed, lying at a height of about 30 miles. This belt would act as a reflector of sound waves.

Actually the temperature 30 miles up has proved to be as high as +170 degrees Fahrenheit, but it must not be

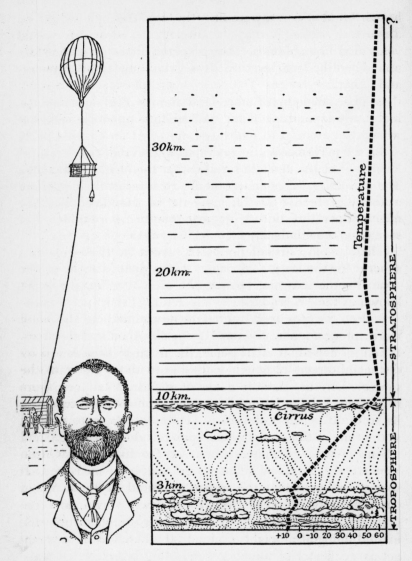

Léon Philippe Teisserenc de Bort and his visualization of the upper atmosphere about fifty years ago. He divided the upper air into two distinct zones, the Troposphere and the Stratosphere.

supposed that a craft passing through the belt would be heated so violently that its unfortunate occupants would be boiled like potatoes. The confusion arises from that fact that scientific "temperature" is not the same thing as everyday "heat."

A gas is made up of atoms and atom-groups or molecules, and the temperature of the gas depends upon the speed at which the atoms and molecules move. At an altitude of 30 miles the movements are very rapid, and so the "temperature" is high—yet the air is so rarefied that the heat which a man would feel on his skin, assuming that he could live there without protective clothing, would be inappreciable. The high-temperature belt is of great scientific importance, but it is in no way dangerous.

There is no particular mystery about it. It is due to a relative concentration of ozone gas, a special form of the more familiar oxygen, between 12 and 21 miles above the ground. Ozone is produced by the action of short-wave radiation from the Sun upon normal oxygen atoms, and the result of the process is that the radiation is absorbed and the "temperature" raised. It is fortunate for us that the ozone layer forms an ultraviolet screen, since otherwise no life would be possible on the surface of the Earth. In small quantities ultraviolet light is beneficial, as is shown by the special lamps to be found in all hospitals; in larger quantities it is lethal, and we are entirely dependent upon our ozone screen.

Clearly the stratosphere was not the simple structure that Teisserenc de Bort had believed, and further research showed that it ended at about 20 miles. From 20 to 50 miles lies the zone recently called the chemosphere. This region contains the ozone layer. Above the chemosphere begins the ionosphere which extends up to about 250 miles. In the ionosphere we find the radio-wave-reflecting layers which make long-range wireless communication possible; the most famous of these layers was found as early as 1902 by two independent workers, Kennelly in America and Heaviside in England. Beyond the ionosphere comes the outermost shell. This exosphere, as it is called, has no well-defined border; it simply "thins out" until there are no air molecules left. Its precise borders are unknown at present, but it may extend up to 700 or 800 miles.

Unfortunately the entire air mantle, apart from the troposphere and the lower stratosphere, remained beyond the reach of even the most efficient balloons. All that could be done was to watch demonstrations obligingly provided by nature, such as meteors and aurorae.

A meteor is a small solid body revolving round the Sun like a miniature planet. When drawn "downwards" by the Earth's gravitational pull, a meteor will enter the atmosphere and friction will be set up with the air particles. At a height of 120 miles or so, this friction becomes great enough to make the meteor glow, and as it dashes into the lower and denser air it is destroyed by the heat set up, so that we witness its death and call it a shooting star. Visible trails left by meteors in the ionosphere and stratosphere showed that the upper air is far from calm, and that the thin atmosphere whips along at a rate of over a hundred miles per hour. The rare and beautiful noctilucent clouds, hanging at altitudes of about fifty miles and therefore sunlit even when the lands below are in darkness, also seem to be of meteoric origin.

Aurorae, or polar lights, occur in the ionosphere and exosphere. They are due to electrified particles sent out by the Sun, which are naturally drawn towards the magnetic poles (the geographical poles have nothing directly to do with it) and collide with the rarefied gases of the upper air. The best analogy is the glowing of a vacuum tube when excited by a spark coil. They are best seen in high latitudes, for obvious reasons, and a winter night in Antarctica or North Norway or Canada would indeed be drab without them. On rare occasions, auroral displays of great brilliance can be

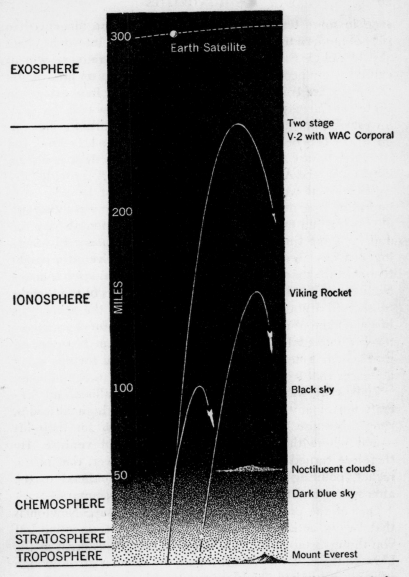

EXOSPHERE

IONOSPHERE

CHEMOSPHERE

STRATOSPHERE

TROPOSPHERE

300 — Earth Satellite

MILES

200

100

50

Two stage
V-2 with WAC Corporal

Viking Rocket

Black sky

Noctilucent clouds

Dark blue sky

Mount Everest

In the left column above are shown the major divisions of the atmosphere; in the right column are shown some major "skymarks."

seen in more temperate zones. The most magnificent display of modern times occurred on January 26, 1938, when the sky in South England shone with a vivid redness which caused many people to think that London was on fire.

Auroræ are true high-altitude phenomena. Researches by Professor Carl Størmer and his colleagues show that the very lowest of them lie at a height of 70 miles, while the loftiest go up to 600 or 700 miles. This means that traces of the exosphere must linger on almost to the old thousand-mile limit set by the Arabs.

Theoretical work of this kind led at least to a general understanding of the atmosphere, but in the words of the old saying "an ounce of practice is worth a ton of theory," and for some time there seemed to be no chance of carrying out any practical experiments at all. Even the high-temperature zone at its altitude of a mere 30 miles was hopelessly out of reach, and the first powered flights of the Wright brothers did not help one iota. Yet in 1903, the same year in which the Wrights flew, a paper by an obscure Russian teacher named Konstantin Ziolkovsky examined the whole problem in a new light, and paved the way for the great advances that were soon to come.

Ziolkovsky was well aware that neither balloons nor aircraft are of any use for the exploration of high altitudes, simply because they are dependent upon air for their lift —and where there is little air, they cannot venture. He therefore turned to a different source of power, that of the rocket, pointing out that a rocket is not confined to the atmosphere and is indeed at its best in total vacuum.

One of the principles laid down by Sir Isaac Newton is that "every action has an equal and opposite reaction." If you thump a table, the blow on your hand is as great as the blow on the table; if you fire a gun, the recoil is great enough to cause a marked "kick" of the barrel. A good way to explain how a rocket works is to picture a man standing on the end of a truck which is mounted on very well oiled rails. If he jumps off, he will move one way while the truck moves in the opposite direction. The movement of the truck is due entirely to the fact that it has been kicked, and the experiment would work just as well in vacuum, assuming that the man could survive there.

Now let us turn to the ordinary Fourth of July skyrocket. Basically it is made up of a cardboard tube filled with gunpowder, and with a hole or exhaust at one end. When the gunpowder is lit it starts to burn, and hot gas is generated. This gas tries to escape from the tube, but can only do so in one direction—through the exhaust. It therefore rushes out in a concentrated stream, kicking the tube of the rocket away from it. In other words, the gas has taken the place of the jumping man and the rocket tube has taken the place of the truck.

The vital point to remember is that air is not concerned in any way. The impetus to the rocket tube is given entirely by reaction, and air is actually a hindrance, since it sets up friction and resistance. Rockets, then, are not limited to the troposphere or even to the stratosphere. Given sufficient fuel, they should be capable of soaring right out into space.

As a matter of fact, it is rather surprising that the principle had not been used for high-altitude work long before the publication of Ziolkovsky's paper. Rockets were known to the Chinese in the thirteenth century, and had even been used in warfare; there are records of a rocket barrage being employed against the Mongols as long ago as 1232, and during the Napoleonic Wars various European nations had developed them, the chief "success" being the rather regrettable bombardment of Copenhagen in 1808. But improvements in more normal artillery had made rockets obsolete, and latterly they had been used only to carry lifelines between the shore and ships in distress. The idea of developing them for scientific research was refreshingly novel.

Ziolkovsky himself never fired a rocket in his life, and his paper attracted little attention; nor did the work of Ganswindt, an enthusiastic but somewhat muddled German amateur who proposed the rocket idea at about the same time. But the seed had been sown, and inevitably it grew. As early as 1908 a brilliant, retiring American scientist, Dr. Robert Hutchings Goddard, commenced a serious study of the problem. Eleven years later he produced his first report, a slim monograph entitled "A Method of Reaching Extreme Altitudes."

Goddard was under no delusions. He knew quite well that the rocket was the key not only to the upper air, but to the exploration of outer space. To begin with, his thoughts wandered no higher than a few hundreds of miles above the ground; but there can be no doubt that his pioneer work paved the way not only for artificial satellites, but for the realization of Man's ultimate aim of interplanetary flight.

CHAPTER 3

Beyond the Atmosphere

UNTIL the end of the first world war, serious rocketry was entirely divorced from the interplanetary idea. It was true that both Ziolkovsky and Ganswindt had discussed "space ships," but Ziolkovsky's work was almost unknown even in Russia, while Ganswindt's many unsound theories prevented his being taken seriously.

Goddard's classic monograph contained the statement that it might one day be possible to build a rocket which could escape from the Earth altogether, and land upon the Moon. Goddard was not considering a manned vehicle, and he pictured a tiny projectile carrying enough magnesium powder to cause a visible flash when it struck the lunar rocks. However, the whole idea of flight to the Moon caught hold of popular imagination. Henceforth rockets were associated with interplanetary travel, and speculation was apt to run rife.

Goddard was not the man to make rash statements. He had an intense dislike of publicity in any form, but his views were based upon years of careful work, and many of the ideas which he put forward in 1919 require little or no modification to-day.

For one thing, solid propellants are still unreliable for high-altitude research. A solid-propellant rocket is difficult to control. Once the store of explosive is lighted, the burning must continue until the propellant has been completely used up —after which the empty rocket is as powerless as a leaf in a gale. Like Ziolkovsky, Goddard came to the conclusion that the only solution was to abandon solid propellants altogether. He turned instead to liquids.

In a liquid-fuel rocket, the fuel itself (gasoline, for instance) is introduced into a combustion chamber together with the oxidant. The two propellants react together, and the gas produced is ejected from the exhaust in the usual way. Liquid air could be used as an oxidant, but pure liquid oxygen is naturally more effective, and this was the substance employed by Goddard. It is, however, awkward to handle, since it boils at the very low temperature of —183 degrees Centigrade and has to be kept in special containers, while the still more powerful oxidants tested in recent years are usually dangerous and corrosive.

For his gasoline-and-liquid-oxygen arrangement, Goddard was forced to replace the old idea of a "rocket" with the new one of a "rocket motor." Endless refinements had to be introduced, and the practical problems were many. Yet it must be remembered that the rocket motor, like the old Chinese firework, is self-sufficient. It does not need to draw upon an external supply of oxygen, since it carries its own oxidant with it, and neither does its exhaust need anything to "push against" apart from its own tube. Ganswindt, the German amateur who can justly claim to be a pioneer in the field of rocketry, never really grasped this vital point; but both Ziolkovsky and Goddard were well aware of it.

It needs considerable force to lift a solid body to a height of even a hundred miles. If a projectile were fired vertically

PRINCIPLES OF ROCKET POWER

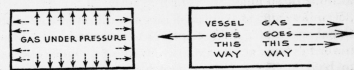

Sealed pressure vessel...no motion. *Vessel open at one end...gas and vessel move in opposite directions.*

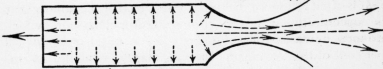

ROCKET MOTOR nozzle speeds up escaping gas, gives more power.

SOLID FUEL rocket motor...fuel is carried within motor. Liquid fuel rocket motor (below)...fuel is outside motor.

LIQUID FUEL ROCKETS

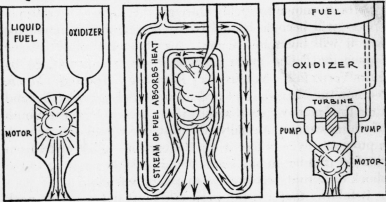

Regenerative cooling (center picture) helps solve problem of intense heat in the motor. Pumping in fuel and oxidizer (right) helps solve the problem of weight. Because fuel tanks are under low pressure and thin-walled, rocket can carry a greater proportion of fuel.

upwards at 1 mile a second, it would theoretically reach an altitude of 90 miles; at a starting speed of 2 miles a second, 350 miles; and at 3 miles a second, 900 miles. If given an initial speed of 7 miles a second (escape velocity) it would never fall back at all, since the Earth's pull would be unable to hold it. These figures, however, neglect one important factor: air resistance.

It is often forgotten that most of the mass of the atmosphere is concentrated near the ground. The troposphere, which extends upwards for only about seven miles, contains 79 per cent of the total mass of the air mantle, while the stratosphere and chemosphere account for 20 per cent and the ionosphere and exosphere between them a mere 1 per cent. Yet the volume percentages are 0.25 or one quarter of one for the troposphere, 2 for the stratosphere and chemosphere, and 97 for the ionosphere and exosphere. If we rise to the top of the stratosphere, we are above 99 per cent of the total atmospheric mass, and by an altitude of 120 miles air resistance has become very slight. In other words, the air thins out very rapidly as we go up.

A body moving quickly through the dense lower troposphere will become heated by friction, and if it moves too fast it will burst into flame. This at once disposes of the "space gun," first made popular nearly a century ago by Jules Verne in his famous story *From the Earth to the Moon*. Verne's travelers were placed inside a hollow projectile, and then fired moonwards at seven miles a second from the mouth of a huge cannon. Actually, air resistance would destroy such a projectile even before it left the cannon—quite apart from the fact that no human frame could possibly stand up to the shock of abrupt acceleration to escape velocity.

It follows that a rising projectile must not reach its peak speed until it has passed through the densest layers of atmosphere, as otherwise troubles due to air resistance will be-

Firing a projectile to the moon at 25,000 m.p.h. At this speed, projectile would be incinerated by friction of air. (See diagram)

From Voyages Extraordinaires "De la Terre a la Lune" by Jules Verne.

come serious. A body fired from a gun must start at maximum velocity, whereas a rocket gathers speed as it climbs.

Unfortunately, even Goddard's liquid fuels could not give sufficient power for such an attempt; nor, for that matter, can the liquid fuels available to-day. Resourceful as ever, Goddard worked on the principle of the "step rocket." As rockets of this type are still of fundamental importance, and will actually be used to launch the first earth satellites, it will be worth while to describe them in some detail.

The basic idea of a two-step arrangement is to mount one rocket on top of another. At the start of the flight the upper rocket does no work, all the power being provided by the motors of the lower, larger component. The bottom "step" uses up its whole store of fuel during the first few miles of ascent, which are always the most perilous. It then breaks free, and after having coasted to the top of its climb it falls back to the ground, leaving the upper step to start its own motors and continue the upward journey. The upper rocket thus starts with two advantages. It is above the worst of the atmosphere, and by the time it begins firing it is already moving at a great speed.

Goddard realized that three- and even four-step rockets are theoretically possible. However, he was no dreamer. He was concerned mainly with upper-atmosphere research, as the title of his 1919 monograph implied, and he was far from pleased at the popular interest in his casual speculation about sending a flash-powder projectile to the Moon. Nor did he mention artificial satellites or space stations, and he was probably unaware of the more futuristic theories put forward by Ziolkovsky.

On January 12, 1920, the *New York Times* printed a front-page story under the headlines "Believes Rocket Can Reach Moon." Further articles followed, and Goddard felt bound to issue a statement clarifying his views. In his own words: "Too much emphasis has been concentrated on the proposed

flash powder experiment, and too little on the atmosphere.
. . . Whatever interesting possibilities there may be for the
method that has been proposed, other than the purpose for
which it was intended, no one of them could be undertaken
without first exploring the atmosphere. Any rocket apparatus

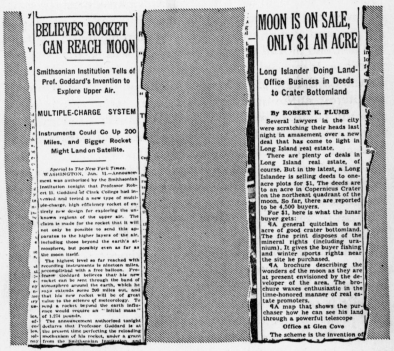

1920 Times clipping (left) and the consequences 36 years later.

for great elevation must first be tested at various moderate
altitudes. Also, a knowledge of the densities at high levels is
essential. Hence, from any point of view, an investigation
of the atmosphere is the work that lies ahead." He added that
the method must be to send up rockets carrying recording
instruments that could subsequently be released and brought

down by parachute, or even by small "braking" rockets which could be fired against the direction of motion and so check the earthward fall.

The interest whipped up by the *New York Times* story and similar newspaper articles did not last, and before long Goddard was left to continue his experiments in peace. On March 16, 1926, he actually fired the first successful liquid-fuel rocket in history. It was powered by gasoline and liquid oxygen, and though it rose to a maximum height of less than 200 feet and moved at only 60 m.p.h., it was of immense significance. It marked the end of an era, and it paved the way for the Earth Satellite program of thirty years later. It caused no interest at the time simply because almost nobody knew about it. Goddard published no report until four years later, and it was not until 1936 that the date and nature of his pioneer experiment became generally known.

Long before then, the world had become thoroughly "rocket conscious." Moreover, the idea of an artificial satellite had been widely popularized, while expressions such as "free fall" and "zero gravity" had become part of everyday vocabulary.

In the illustration of the free fall experiment, which (needless to say) is not to scale, AB is supposed to represent a high tower built upon the surface of the Earth. Its exact altitude is not important apart from the reservation that it must project above the top of the resisting atmosphere. Now suppose that several bullets are fired from B, at various velocities and in a direction parallel to the Earth's surface. The first bullet is fired gently; it soon falls, and lands at C. The second is given a greater starting velocity, and falls to the ground at D, while the third travels some way round the Earth before it lands at E. The fourth bullet, F, is fired at approximately five miles a second. It "falls" continuously, but at the same time the surface of the Earth "falls" away from beneath it, and the result is that the distance of the bullet from the ground remains constant. Eventually the bullet arrives back at the top of the tower, and begins another revolution of the Earth. It has in fact entered a closed satellite orbit, and unless perturbed by some external force it will continue circling indefinitely. The Moon, at its distance of a quarter of a million miles, behaves just like this. Like our hypothetical bullet F, it is moving in "free fall."

A solid body such as the Earth acts as though all its mass were concentrated at its center, and the Earth therefore does its best to draw us downwards. We are always aware of this force, but it is not so generally realized that we feel heavy not because we are placed in a gravitational field but because

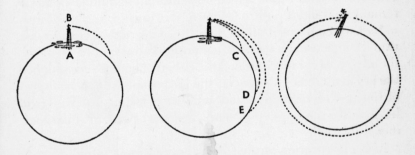

we are resisting this field. A man sitting on a chair is fighting against the Earth's attempt to pull him downwards, and consequently he presses on the seat. Yet heaviness or "weight" is not the same thing as "mass."

To explain this, let us take a sheet of cardboard, place a rubber eraser on top of it, and let it fall. Before the cardboard is dropped the rubber will press on it, but during the fall both board and eraser will be moving in the same direction at the same speed—so that the eraser will cease to press down and will become temporarily "weightless" with respect to the board. Only when the board stops moving does the eraser start to press on it again.

Much the same thing would be experienced by a man who

stepped out of an airplane without taking the precaution of equipping himself with a parachute. Neglecting air resistance, he would feel "weightless" during his descent, because he would be falling freely and would not be resisting the Earth's pull.

Now consider the case of a man inside a hollow projectile circling the Earth in a satellite orbit. Both he and the projectile are moving in the same direction at the same speed, so that the man will not press on the floor of the projectile any more than the rubber pressed on the falling board. Nor will he feel the Earth's pull, since he is not resisting it. He will consequently be in the weightless condition of "zero gravity"; yet his mass, the amount of matter in his body, will remain unaltered.

In this connection it is worth noting that Jules Verne, usually so accurate, made a serious mistake here. In his story, the adventurers became weightless only when they reached the point at which the Earth's gravitational pull balances that of the Moon. Actually, the occupants of the projectile would have been weightless from the moment that they left the mouth of their cannon.

The first man to present theories of this type in scientific form was a Romanian, Professor Hermann Oberth. In 1923 Oberth, then a completely unknown mathematics teacher, wrote a slim booklet entitled *Rakete zu den Planetenräumen* (*The Rocket into Interplanetary Space*), which raised the whole subject of space travel from vague speculation to true science. The booklet was issued by the Munich firm of R. Oldenbourg, after several other publishers had refused it, and despite its mathematical nature it became widely known.

The remarkable thing about Oberth's book was that it was entirely original. Goddard had published nothing but his one cautious monograph; Ziolkovsky had been more prolific, but his papers had never been translated, and Professor Oberth could not read Russian. (He still cannot, as he told me when

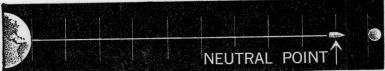

NEUTRAL POINT

Zero gravity in the Jules Verne Moon projectile at the "neutral point" where Earth gravity balances Moon gravity. Actual "floating" inside a space ship would occur when the motors were shut off.

I last talked to him a year or two ago, before his departure from Europe to the United States.)

The first section of the book contained an account of the mathematical aspects of rocketry, and the second was an equally technical description of a proposed rocket for upper-atmosphere research. The third section, however, was of different character. Oberth not only discussed interplanetary flight and space-stations, but went into minor problems such as vacuum suits and methods of overcoming the awkwardness of zero-gravity conditions.

There was nothing eccentric or scatterbrained about Oberth. His book was a sound mathematical treatise, and it caused a revolution in scientific thought. Interplanetary Societies sprang up like mushrooms, first in Germany and then in other countries, and sober and realistic views were swamped in a general wave of enthusiasm.

Oberth was not responsible for this. Unlike Goddard he was not a practical experimenter, but he had at least shown the way. He foresaw that the first orbital vehicles would be launched during his own lifetime, and it is hardly likely that the 1955 announcement came as any surprise to him.

CHAPTER 4

Development of High-Altitude Rockets

Once an artificial satellite has been placed in a sufficiently high orbit round the Earth it cannot fall back to the ground. Nor will it need any application of power to keep it moving; if its orbit is entirely outside the Earth's atmosphere, it will be in free fall, and will in fact behave in just the same way as a natural astronomical body like the Moon.

On the other hand, a great deal of power must be necessary to launch the satellite. Since this can be provided only by the rocket motor, rocketry is an essential part of the satellite program, and when we trace the story back to its beginnings we are bound to come back to the practical work of Goddard and the theories of Ziolkovsky and Oberth.

Actually, Oberth's book was the greatest single factor in the awakening of general interest. Appropriately enough Germany took the lead, and in 1927 a group of men in Breslau founded the famous VfR or Verein für Raumschiffahrt, the Society for Space Travel. It was not the first of the world's interplanetary societies (that distinction seems to belong to a short-lived Moscow group of 1924), but it was the first which tried to undertake practical work. It lasted for only a few years, but it had far-reaching effects.

The VfR was not content to deal only with the upper atmosphere. As the name suggests, it was concerned with the future exploration of other worlds, beginning of course with the Moon. Oberth belonged to it, and for a time even acted as its president, but the bulk of the work was carried out by a small group of men at a testing ground near Berlin known as the Raketenflugplatz or Rocket Flying Field. On March 14, 1931, an independent worker named Johannes Winkler, the original president of the VfR, was successful in firing a small liquid-fuel rocket to a height of several hundreds of feet. It has been described as looking like "a prism placed on end," and had three tanks, containing respectively liquid oxygen, liquid methane, and compressed nitrogen. Shortly afterwards the workers at the Raketenflugplatz were equally successful. At that time almost nothing was known about Goddard's work, and the Germans naturally assumed that their liquid-fuel arrangements were the first of their kind.

Unfortunately the VfR, like all amateur scientific societies, was in constant financial difficulty. Various money-raising schemes were unsuccessful, and by 1933 the Society had ceased to exist—due partly to lack of funds and partly to the changing political situation in Germany. Some of the Raketenflugplatz workers went to America, while others (notably Wernher von Braun) joined the research group on military rockets. Meanwhile another association had been formed in the United States. It was first known as the American Interplanetary Society, but it soon found this name to be a disadvantage. Rockets might be taken seriously, but space flight was still pure fantasy, and before long the title was changed to the American Rocket Society.

As a matter of fact, true interplanetary travel was once more coming to be regarded as a pipe dream. Goddard's paper and Oberth's book had led some people to suppose that a trip to the Moon was imminent; once it was realized that a tremendous number of technical problems remained to be solved before even the upper atmosphere could be reached, reaction set in. The situation was not helped by a growing river of horrific, badly written "science fiction," and the pulp magazines produced between 1927 and 1939 did rocket science a grave disservice. Such literature lasted until the end of the war, and even now a certain amount of it is produced.

When the full story of those early days comes to be written, historians of the future will find much to amuse them. There was, for instance, the extraordinary episode of the Magdeburg Experiment of 1933. An eccentric "scientist" had written a paper showing that the Earth itself is nothing more than the interior of a hollow sphere, and pointing out that in this case a rocket sent vertically upwards would crash-land eventually in the Antipodes. Amazingly enough the City Council agreed to the experiment being made, even though it seems unlikely that they had much faith in the hollow-sphere theory; and a rocket was actually built. Unfortunately it rose to a maximum height of only six feet, so that the experiment can hardly be regarded as conclusive! *

In the same year, the British Interplanetary Society was formed at the instigation of P. E. Cleator. Nowadays the Society is rightly regarded as an eminent and learned body, but in 1933 it was not taken in the least seriously. Nor, for that matter, was jet propulsion. In a famous letter written in the following year to one of the Society's officials, the

* I cannot resist quoting a really weird idea which was put to me in all seriousness only a few months ago. The author of it realized that a helicopter can "hover," and he planned to build a giant helicopter that would be able to hover for years on end. He suggested that the right way to get to Mars was to take the helicopter up to a height of several miles and simply let it stay there; the Earth would move off on its path round the Sun, so that all the space travelers would have to do would be to wait until Mars came along, when they could drop calmly down . . .

British Under-Secretary of State for Air wrote that with regard to the jet engine "scientific investigation into the possibilities has given no indication that the method can be a serious competitor to the airscrew-engine combination," and added that Britain was not justified in wasting time or money on jet research. Moreover, there was no Raketenflug-platz available. Every attempt at practical work was suppressed by the Explosives Act of 1875, and to this day the Society has had to remain a theoretical body only.

One or two well-known scientists (such as Professor A. M. Low) were more far-sighted, and somehow the Society managed to survive until the outbreak of war. In 1939 hostilities began, and in Britain at least all interplanetary research came to a halt. The Society did not disband, but it suspended all activities for the duration.

The situation in Germany was very different. The VfR had died, but rocket research was in full swing—not for the purpose of space travel, but for military use. The famous research station at Peenemünde, on the Baltic coast, already existed. High-altitude experiments had already been confused by the introduction of the interplanetary theme; now they were to be still further complicated by the warlike plans of the Nazis.

The moving spirit behind Peenemünde was a soldier, Colonel (afterwards Major-General) Walter Dornberger. Dornberger had paid several visits to the VfR Raketenflug-platz, and although he was unimpressed by much of what he saw he did realize that the liquid-fuel rocket could be turned into a devastating weapon. Backed by the war department he set up his own experimental station at Kummersdorf, near Berlin, and on the break-up of the VfR the leading pioneers joined him there. The first Kummersdorf rocket motor was tested towards the end of 1932. It was not a success, inasmuch as it exploded and wrecked both itself and its testing rack, but Dornberger was not discouraged.

Two years later a liquid-fuel rocket soared almost a mile and a half into the air.

One of Dornberger's team, Wernher von Braun, was quick to realize that inland sites such as Kummersdorf were severely limited. Rockets are both noisy and spectacular, and for their military development it was of course vital to work in secret. He therefore suggested the removal of the entire project to Peenemünde, a small village on the Baltic island of Usedom. Oddly enough von Braun was not the first man to select this area for rocket research. Eight years before, Professor Oberth had asked permission to fire a rocket from the nearby islet of Griefswalder Oie, and had been refused on the grounds that he might damage the local lighthouse!

The Peenemünde project was soon under way. By December 1937 experimental launchings had begun; on October 3, 1942, came the first successful ascent of the rocket which was known originally as the A4, but which achieved notoriety as the V2. The ascent was watched by Dornberger and von Braun—also by Oberth, who had arrived at Peenemünde a few days earlier but who had not actually played a part in the V2 program. Their feelings were aptly summed up by Dornberger in the following words: "The experiment had succeeded. For the first time in the history of the rocket we had flown an automatically guided, jet-driven projectile as far as the limit of the atmosphere and sent it on into practically airless space."

The maximum height of the first V2 was 60 miles, so that it reached the top of the chemosphere. (The record altitude for a shell fired from a gun stood, incidentally, at a mere 25 miles.) Later V2s attained well over 110 miles. Since measurable atmospheric resistance becomes very slight above 120 miles, it can be claimed that these projectiles were Man's first messengers into space.

The V2 was, of course, powered by a liquid-fuel motor. The entire middle section of the rocket was reserved for the tanks containing the propellants. The upper tank contained 3¾ tons of ethyl alcohol, suitably diluted with water, and the lower held 5 tons of liquid oxygen. These propellants were forced into the combustion chamber by powerful pumps, and since it was necessary to deliver 37 gallons of propellant per second into the chamber when the motor was running at full power these pumps were not at all easy to design. The temperature of the inner chamber (over 3,500 degrees Fahrenheit) raised extra problems.

The total weight of the fully-fuelled V2 was 14 tons. The rocket was 40 feet long, and its general appearance is shown on page 52.

It is often thought that a rocket has reached maximum height when its entire store of fuel is exhausted. This is not so. The moment of burn-out, or Brennschluss, to use a German word which is finding its way into our own language, merely marks the end of powered flight; the velocity gained causes the rocket to go on rising until it is finally stopped by the persistent pull of the Earth. The best analogy is to picture a pedal-cyclist making his way up a short, steep hill. If he gathers enough speed before starting the climb, he can stop pedaling halfway and still coast over the top of the hill, because at the moment when he stops pedaling —his Brennschluss—he is moving at considerable velocity.

The importance of the work at Peenemünde was that it turned theory into practice. The V2s were very different from Goddard's early attempts and from the primitive rockets fired from the Raketenflugplatz, and it had become clear that Goddard's "method of reaching extreme altitudes" was a sound one. The Nazi Command was not in the least interested in high-altitude study or space ships, but the Peenemünde scientists were; and the result was that in early 1944 the secret police, the Gestapo of evil memory, pounced upon Peenemünde and arrested von Braun and two of his assistants upon a charge of paying too much attention to space flight and too little to developing a military weapon.

Probably the charge was only an excuse for the Gestapo to interfere in the running of Peenemünde, and Dornberger had little difficulty in putting matters right, but the episode is significant. Only military considerations could force any government to provide enough money for rocket research.

Peenemünde had already had one severe setback. During 1942 the Allies became aware that Germany was preparing a new weapon, and Hitler at least was not bound by the wording of the Explosives Act of 1875. Accordingly the Royal Air Force carried out a major raid on the proving ground. During the night of August 17, 1943, some fifteen hundred tons of high-explosive bombs were dropped, as well as many incendiaries, and over 800 workers were killed— the chief casualty being Dr. Thiel, head of the propulsion department.

Incidentally, it should be added that the V1s—known popularly as the "buzz-bombs" or "doodle-bugs"—were not true rockets at all. They depended upon oxygen drawn from the atmosphere, and were limited to low levels. Nor were they developed by the Peenemünde team.

Had the rocket experimenters been given full support earlier in the war, it is certain that the rockets would have led to far more Allied casualties than they actually did. However, Hitler and his advisers were skeptical; the research station was very expensive to maintain, and Peenemünde fought constant battles with the Treasury. When Hitler at last changed his mind, the pendulum swung right over— and Peenemünde was expected to produce a war-winning weapon in a matter of a few months. The task was impossible, and although fifteen hundred V2s were aimed at London between September 1944 and March 1945 they did no more than add destruction to the already battered city. Germany as a military power was already doomed by the time that the V2 was operational.

When hostilities ended at last, the Peenemünde team was broken up. Most of its leading members, including Dornberger and von Braun, departed for America to continue research there, to be joined ten years later by Professor Oberth. But despite the evil use to which the V2 was put, it represented a great scientific advance. Dornberger himself summed matters up when he wrote: "A dream can now become a reality; the space ship can emerge out of hopes and theories."

CHAPTER 5

Ten Years of Progress

A GREAT deal of nonsense has been written about "space ships." The very word makes one think of a long, sleek craft shaped like a bullet, with tapering wings and gently purring motors, while the absent-minded professor of fiction invariably builds his machine in his own back garden and fires himself off to the Moon without making enough noise to alarm the neighbors. The actual ship, when it is built, will not be at all like this, but the first essential is to decide exactly what is meant by the term. Considered from some points of view, the V2 is a space ship. It is powered by rocketry, and at the peak of its climb it soars to near the limit of the resisting atmosphere.

This latter point was made many times after the end of the war, and inevitably some people jumped to the conclusion that the Moon was almost within reach. (Oberth's book had had much the same effect over twenty years before.) The flood of dubious science fiction continued, and some of the "serious" articles that appeared in papers and journals between 1945 and 1947 make amusing reading. But the general

situation had changed. Research was no longer left to amateurs, even brilliant amateurs such as those who had experi-
mented at the Raketenflugplatz. It had become a military
necessity to develop high-altitude rockets, and all the Great
Powers knew it.

It was natural for the United States to take the lead; her
homeland had not been ravaged by war, whereas it took
Britain years to heal her wounds. Moreover, the United
States had the money to spend on rocket research, as well as
the good sense to obtain the services of German experts such
as von Braun. A proving ground was established at White
Sands, in New Mexico, well away from large towns and
cities, and work was begun without delay.

A moment's thought will show that the setting-up of a
similar ground in the British Isles is out of the question. One
of the troubles about a rocket is that it is difficult to control
once it has left the ground. Remote-control systems can do
much, but mishaps are always liable to occur. On one occa-
sion, for instance, a White Sands rocket was seen to be head-
ing straight for an inhabited area; actually it did no harm,
but the episode served as a warning.

Britain's own proving ground was finally set up at Woomera in Australia, where there are vast stretches of unpopu-
lated desert. The first tests were carried out in the autumn
of 1949, and have continued steadily up to the present day.
Nor were the Russians idle. Some of the Peenemünde workers elected to throw in their lot with the East rather than
with the West, but even now the first lifting of the Iron Curtain has not revealed many details of postwar Soviet experiments.

White Sands is not the only American rocket ground, as is
so often supposed, but it is certainly the most famous. It lies
in New Mexico, below the foothills of the Organ Mountains
which form a fitting background to it. Before the arrival of
the research workers it was a lonely desert, with typical

scrub vegetation and no natural inhabitants apart from jack-rabbits and other small animals. Nowadays the scene is very different, and concrete blockhouses rear up from the desert sands, while the calm is broken at intervals by the roaring of rocket motors under test.

During the tense years after the War, no casual visitors were allowed at White Sands—and in fact this rule still applies. Information was released sparingly, and usually not until it was out of date. Enough was learned, however, to make people realize that the rocket had come to stay.

The unused V2s left over from the war proved to be extremely useful as research vehicles. However, they had their limitations, and scientific workers naturally wanted something better. In time came the development of the Viking rocket, in some ways similar to the V2 but representing an entirely independent and new engineering achievement. It is not possible to tell the story of this rocket in a few lines, or even a few pages; suffice to say that it was in every way a magnificent research tool, and had only one real disadvantage—its expense. Every Viking firing cost several hundreds of thousands of dollars; consequently the firings had to be infrequent, though they paid for themselves many times over in terms of the information gathered from them. Much cheaper was the Aerobee, an uncontrolled liquid-fuel rocket launched from a hundred-foot tower assisted by a solid propellant "booster" not unlike the jet-assisted take-off units used for aircraft.

It was at White Sands, in 1949, that the first step rocket was actually fired. The ascent was witnessed by none of the three great pioneers; Ziolkovsky and Goddard were dead, Oberth still in Europe. However, it was a complete success. The large "booster," or lower component, was simply a German V2 with its warhead removed, while the small upper rocket was known as a WAC Corporal. Unaided, the WAC would have been able to rise to an altitude of something like

MAJOR U. S. RESEARCH ROCKETS

*The American Rocket Society (ARS) Rocket No. 2
represents a primitive stage in rocket development.
The Aerobee was designed specifically as a
research rocket. The Aerobee-Hi (not shown) is
expected to reach 185 miles. The V-2 has gone up
114 miles — with the WAC Corporal, 250 miles. The
Viking rose 158 miles. Vanguard will carry the
satellite into orbit. Not shown are Deacon, a
balloon-launched rocket and Hermes, an Americanized
version of the V-2.*

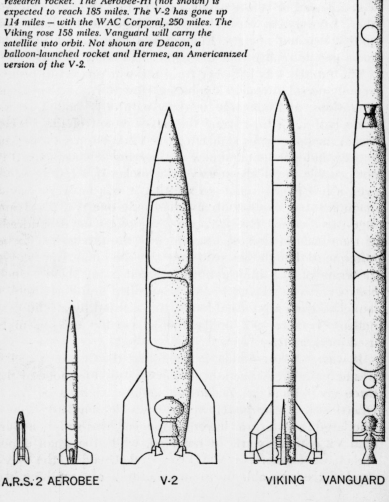

A.R.S. 2   AEROBEE   V-2   VIKING   VANGUARD

50 miles. Actually it did not start its own motors until it had been carried up to 20 miles on the top of the V2, and when the V2 broke away, to fall back to the ground with its mission accomplished, the WAC soared on to a total altitude of almost 250 miles.

The atmosphere at a height of 250 miles is so tenuous that it can be regarded as virtual vacuum. In other words, the WAC Corporal had reached interplanetary space. It carried no warhead, and was purely a scientific vehicle, but it proved what the much-ridiculed pioneers had said so long before.

On the other hand the WAC Corporal was a tiny thing, unable to carry much in the way of equipment. Calculations were made with regard to the possibility of launching the V2 itself; with available propellants the dead weight of the lower component worked out at over 200 tons. A three-step arrangement, keeping the V2 as the smallest member of the trio, would mean an initial launcher weighing over 5,000 tons.

Interesting results were nevertheless obtained. One of the most spectacular was the photographing of the Earth from great altitudes. One of the first photographs released was taken by an automatic camera mounted in a V2, showing the Earth as seen from a height of 60 miles (the top of the chemosphere). The distance shown along the horizon amounted to 1,400 miles, stretching from Upper Wyoming to Mexico, and the curvature of the globe was very obvious.*

Of greater importance were attempts to solve some of the problems which could not be attacked from ground level. There was, for instance, the question of radiations which are normally blocked out by the atmosphere.

The unit of wavelength is known as the angström, and is equal to one hundred millionth part of a centimetre, so that it is very minute. The human eye is sensitive to light be-

* One result of this and similar pictures was to hasten the death of the last Flat Earth Societies, some of which flourished as recently as 1946!

tween wavelengths of 7,500 and 4,000 angströms, and this is what we mean by "visible" light. Infrared and ultraviolet techniques can extend the range to either side of this boundary, but below about 2,900 angströms we can go no further; shorter wavelengths are cut off by the air. Towards the long-

Portion of the earth's surface seen from a rocket 100 miles up. The spiral configuration is a hurricane 1000 miles in diameter.

wave end, the limiting wavelength is 30,000 angströms. The interval between 2,900 and 30,000 angströms is thus known as the "optical window," and there is a second interval (the "radio window") between wavelengths of 1 centimetre and about 40 metres. We are thus in the position of a man who cannot move his head and is limited to making observations through two narrow transparent slits in an otherwise opaque wall.

Although rockets could not carry human observers high enough to let them make direct observations from above the absorbing layers, it seemed possible to equip rockets with photographic and recording equipment which would make available the normally blocked-out regions of the Sun's spectrum. Experiments began in a modest way as far back as 1946, and were encouraging. Unfortunately the method had two severe limitations. The rockets remained above the barrier for brief periods only, and since each rocket costs a great deal of money the process was an expensive one. Secondly, there was the problem of recovering the instruments after they had fallen back to the ground. They were generally located without much difficulty, but were frequently so damaged that they and their records were of no use.

Another problem was that of high-altitude winds. The air movements in the troposphere and lower chemosphere had, of course, been studied by older methods, such as balloons, but the new experiments extended the field of operations into the ionosphere as well.

The composition of the upper air was also studied. A former theory had held that most of the atmospheric oxygen and nitrogen was confined to low levels, so that in its upper reaches the "air" was made up mainly of lighter gases such as hydrogen and helium. There were grounds for such an idea, since hydrogen is by far the most abundant element in the universe, but the rocket tests showed it to be false. As far up as could be measured, the atmosphere appeared to be of the same percentage composition as at sea-level.

Another line of research concerned solid bodies in space which are prevented by the atmosphere from reaching the ground. The Solar System, as we know, is made up principally of one normal star (the Sun), nine major planets, thirty-one moons or satellites of the major planets, and about 45,000 minor planets which are confined mainly to a belt lying between the orbits of Mars and Jupiter. Yet "cosmic débris" in the form of meteors is very plentiful, and shooting stars can be seen any night of the year.

It is wrong to suppose that the average shooting star is a large body. Even a brilliant one is smaller than a golf ball, and most are comparable with grains of dust. The giants that survive the complete drop, to be picked up subsequently as meteorites, are extremely rare.

Estimates of the numbers of "micrometeorites," as the smallest bodies are termed, could be carried out by rocket exploration. Preliminary results indicated that meteor dangers to future space-craft or artificial satellites were less than had been supposed, and that the fear of destruction by cosmical shellfire had been exaggerated. The micrometeorites proved to be numerous indeed, but so tiny that they could do little harm.

Just as a sheep, a cock and a duck were the first passengers in the primitive balloon of 1783, so animals were selected for the first terrestrial space travelers. After a series of preliminary experiments, mice and monkeys were sent up to the dizzy height of 80 miles, and when picked up seemed to be none the worse. Photographs taken during the descent by means of an automatic camera showed the mice floating about in their compartment under conditions of zero gravity. This film was subsequently released for public showing, and did much to allay the fears of those who were still dubious about high-altitude flight.

If mice and monkeys can ascend into the ionosphere, men can presumably follow; but the human body is not adapted to conditions in a near-vacuum, and is likely to be the weakest link in the chain. Accordingly the Americans set up a department of "space medicine" specifically to deal with such problems.

Actually, the problems themselves were not new, and most of them had been met with during experiments with normal aircraft. The present height record for a human being is

First man into the stratosphere. On May 27, 1931, the balloon of A. Piccard reached 51,775 feet.

Highest balloonists. Anderson and Stevens rose 72,395 feet Nov. 11, 1935. Present record

Highest man, Maj. Arthur Murray. On June 16, 1954 his Bell X-1A climbed to 90,000 ft. (17 mi.)

Highest monkey. "Mike" went up 36 mi. in 1952. His wife, "Pat" went with him, has since died.

about 90,000 feet (17 miles), the machine used being a Bell X-1A, which is in fact a cross between an aircraft and a space ship. For all practical purposes a height of 17 miles is equivalent to outer space with regard to the behavior of the human body, since all the major problems are first met with at lower altitudes.

The first trouble which faced the pioneer aviators was lack of oxygen. Above 12,000 feet or so * the supply of this vital

* The maximum altitude of endurance varies with different people. I personally could never go above 12,000 feet without using oxygen, but my wartime wireless operator could manage at 15,000 feet without feeling any appreciable discomfort. These figures are, of course, those for sudden ascent; when climbing a mountain, one has time to become accustomed to the changing conditions.

gas is too small to maintain life, and special precautions must be taken. The remedy here was to develop a simple oxygen mask, and this proved sufficient for altitudes up to more than 35,000 feet. Then, however, another trouble arose owing to the functional system of the lung.

The pressure inside a man's lung is maintained partly by oxygen drawn in, and partly by gases such as carbon dioxide and water vapor produced inside the body. The pressure is always kept at a constant level, and if the oxygen pressure is low more carbon dioxide and water vapor will be produced to compensate for it. The standard lung pressure is about 87 mm. of mercury. If therefore the outside atmospheric pressure drops to this value, no outside air—and therefore no oxygen—can enter the lungs at all.

Theoretically this occurs at a height of 52,000 feet, but practically the trouble begins much earlier. The simple oxygen mask is no longer sufficient. This time the remedy proved to be pressure breathing and pressurized cabins, and the latter became absolutely necessary at 63,000 feet, where yet a third danger is met with.

The pressure of the air at 63,000 feet is a mere 47 mm. of mercury. Most people know that the boiling point of a liquid depends upon the pressure on it, so that water boils at 212 degrees Fahrenheit at sea-level but at only 186 degrees on the top of Everest. Blood, too, can boil; at 63,000 feet it would boil at a temperature of only 98.4 degrees Fahrenheit, which is the normal temperature of the body. A man who ventured above this altitude without a pressurized cabin or suit would consequently find the blood boiling in his veins literally as well as metaphorically, and death would follow in a matter of seconds.

All these knotty problems were studied by the Space Medicine Department, and their occasional reports showed that real progress was being made—even with respect to that much-ridiculed garment the space suit, which is as necessary at 15 miles as it is at 500 unless the pilot is enclosed in a special cabin.

Needless to say, the main emphasis at White Sands and Woomera was not upon actual space flight. Interplanetary journeys still lay in the future; von Braun and others did produce elaborate plans of manned satellites, lunar bases and full-scale expeditions to Mars, but they knew that exploration of the upper air must come first.

There is no easy road to the planets. Each step must be worked out years in advance, and there is need for caution. The first step was the high-altitude rocket, which had already paid rich dividends but which was limited in scope by its cost, its instability, and the shortness of its period in space. The second step could only be the small unmanned artificial satellite, and as long ago as 1948 an official Earth Satellite Vehicle program was inaugurated by the United States Government.

CHAPTER 6

Orbital Vehicles

THE IDEA of an artificial satellite is not new. Once again, it is first found in fiction, and the earliest definite references to a "space station" occur in a novel published in 1897. Its title was *Auf Zwei Planeten* (*On Two Planets*), and it was written by Kurd Laszwitz, Professor of Mathematics at Gotha. It was reprinted as recently as 1948 (the centenary of Laszwitz's birth), and although many of the ideas contained in it are fantastic it is well worth reading, particularly as it was written before the work of such pioneers as Ziolkovsky and Ganswindt became known.

Ganswindt himself had some rather confused ideas about space stations, and it was not until the appearance of Professor Oberth's classic *Rakete zu den Planetenräumen,* in 1923, that the idea was treated in a scientific manner. Here again Oberth's brilliance was evident. He knew little or nothing about the earlier work, and the theory developed was entirely his own.

One of the facts realized by Oberth was that if travel

in space is to become fact, there must be some provision for refueling a rocket beyond the atmosphere. Even by the use of the step method, no vehicle powered by liquid fuels (at least liquid fuels of the type known in 1923) would have any chance of breaking free from the Earth and keeping enough power reserve to take off from the Moon again on the return journey. On the other hand, by far the greater part of the fuel store must be used up in the initial blast-off from ground level; most of the quarter-million-mile journey to the Moon would be done in free fall, no fuel expenditure being necessary.

Oberth therefore saw that if a rocket could blast away from the immediate vicinity of the Earth with its tanks full and its initial ascent over, a lunar voyage might become a real possibility. The journey would be done in three stages: Earth to space-station, station to Moon, and Moon back to Earth.

Oberth's pioneer work was followed up by a Viennese engineer, Count Guido von Pirquet, who developed the idea of a proper manned satellite to serve not only as a refueling point but as a laboratory and observatory. Von Pirquet knew that such a satellite was little more than a dream; at that period the VfR was in existence, and the Raketenflugplatz workers were experimenting with their tiny liquid-fuel arrangements unaware that Goddard was doing the same thing in America. But at least there was nothing absurd in the general principle, and the space-station idea became an accepted part of the interplanetary project.

The notion of a "celestial refuelling station," a sort of filling station beyond the atmosphere, was an attractive one —and before the war began in 1939 a good many designs and blueprints for it had been produced by earnest enthusiasts. Some of these designs were reasonable enough, but it was, of course, clear that they were highly futuristic. The manned space station was bound to be preceded by un-

SPACE STATION EVOLUTION

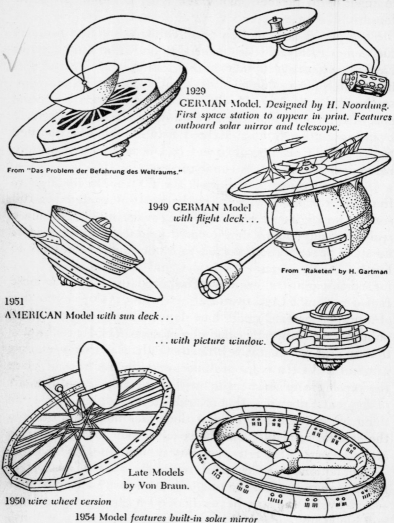

1929 GERMAN Model. *Designed by H. Noordung. First space station to appear in print. Features outboard solar mirror and telescope.*

From "Das Problem der Befahrung des Weltraums."

1949 GERMAN Model *with flight deck...*

From "Raketen" by H. Gartman

1951
AMERICAN Model *with sun deck...*

...with picture window.

Late Models
by Von Braun.

1950 *wire wheel version*

1954 Model *features built-in solar mirror*

Since 1929 most concepts of a manned satellite station have favored circular design. To date, none have been built. Expense—a big factor. A late model Von Braun costs 4½ billion dollars.

manned high-altitude missiles, revolving at heights of a few hundreds of miles.

The first official mention of an artificial satellite came in December 1948, with the Forrestal Report. The United States Defense Secretary at that time was James V. Forrestal, a man with considerable scientific knowledge and unusual foresight. Forrestal himself was a firm believer in eventual space flight, and when he presented the annual report to Congress on the National Military Establishment he revealed that an earth satellite program had actually been inaugurated. (The White House announcement of 1955 was merely a logical development of the plan.) Naturally enough in those days of the intensive "cold war," the satellite was intended for military use; but it was emphasized that science would benefit as well. It was to be a meteorological station, an astronomical observatory, a radar beacon, a television relay, a "hard vacuum" laboratory and a chemical and biological research center, as well as a means of sending fully fueled rockets into deep space.

If the Forrestal Report had done nothing else, it would at least have shown that the idea of an artificial satellite was not the pipe dream of a few fanatics. It is true that a manned satellite will be a colossal undertaking, quite beyond us at the present time, but for a small unmanned satellite many of the worst problems do not arise at all.

For instance, no provision need be made for keeping the vehicle airtight—and this would be a difficult matter. Nor need any fuel be kept in reserve for landing, since the projectile would never return to Earth; once set in orbit it would continue circling for ever, unless interfered with naturally or artificially. It need not even carry fuel of its own —it could be launched from the upper component of a step rocket, and so long as its instruments remained capable of functioning it would continue to relay information back to the ground. Also, a small unmanned vehicle could be built in a laboratory and sent directly into orbit, whereas a manned station would have to be assembled in space under conditions of free fall.

It must always be borne in mind that as soon as an artificial satellite has been set in its stable orbit, it must become an astronomical body—and hence subject to the usual laws of planetary motion. These laws were first stated by Kepler in the early seventeenth century, at about the same time as the invention of the telescope. The most important one from our point of view states that the further a planet is from the Sun, the less must be its orbital speed. Little Mercury, at a mere 36 million miles, moves along at about 30 miles a second, whereas the Earth (93 million miles from the Sun) moves at a more modest 18½ miles a second, and remote Pluto (3,666 million miles) at only 3 miles a second. This law also applies to the satellites of the major planets. Saturn, for example, has nine moons; the innermost (Mimas) is the fastest-moving, and the outermost (Phœbe) the slowest.

A projectile skimming around the Earth in a circular path just above the limit of air resistance would have to move at 5 miles a second in order to remain in a stable orbit. Further out, it would move more slowly, and at a distance of 238,000 miles it would crawl along at only two-thirds of a mile a second—which is the speed of the true Moon, whose actual distance is in fact 238,000 miles. It makes no difference whether the body concerned is made of rock or solid steel.

The Earth turns on its axis once in every 24 hours (more accurately, 23 hours 57 minutes). A satellite lying at a distance of 200 miles would revolve round the Earth in 90 minutes, and to a terrestrial observer would appear to rise in the west and set in the east. As the distance increases, so does the length of the revolution period, known astronomically as the "periodic time." For a distance of 22,000 miles, the periodic time would be 24 hours, and provided that the satellite had been originally placed above the equator it would appear to be fixed in the heavens, always keeping above the same spot on the ground. Beyond 22,000 miles the periodic time would exceed 24 hours, so that the satellite would rise in the east and set in the west in the usual fashion.

There is an interesting analogy here with Mars. The Red Planet has two moons, Phobos and Deimos, both of which are less than a dozen miles across. The axial rotation of Mars is only half an hour longer than our own; Phobos, at a distance of a mere 3,700 miles above the surface, speeds round in 7 hours 39 minutes, which is only one-third the length of a Martian day. To an observer on Mars, Phobos would move across the sky from west to east, taking only 4½ hours to pass from horizon to horizon and going through more than half its cycle of phases in the process. Deimos, at 12,500 miles, has a revolution period of 30 hours, which is not much longer than the Martian day. As Mars spins, therefore, Deimos almost keeps pace with it, falling behind only very slowly; and consequently a Martian observer would see it above the horizon for 2½ "days" at a time.*

Needless to say, the first unmanned satellites will be set up at distances of much less than 22,000 miles, and in any case their orbits will not be simple circles. It would in fact be very difficult to set a satellite in a perfectly circular path, and the actual orbit will be an ellipse of greater or less eccentricity. This leads to some rather interesting possibilities. If a satellite "dipped into" the resisting atmosphere when at its nearest point to the Earth, it would lose a certain amount of speed at each revolution, and so it would be

* Flying saucer enthusiasts have suggested that the curious behavior of the two tiny moons is an indication that the Martians, too, have turned their thoughts towards the construction of space-stations—so that the first visitors from Earth are likely to find satellites made of metal rather than rock! No comment seems to be required.

gradually brought down until it burned itself up in the manner of a shooting star, though the process might take weeks or even months, depending upon the original height of the orbit above ground level.

Plans and proposals were not slow to follow the Forrestal Report, and when the International Astronautical Federation met in London in 1951 some twenty papers were sub-

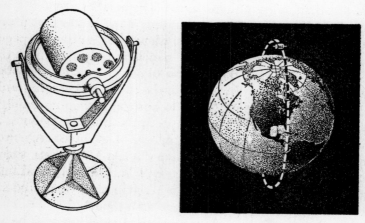

Model of the MOUSE and its proposed polar orbit. Mounted on a gimbal, it can be directed to orient itself toward the Sun.

mitted on the subject. In 1954 a detailed description of a proposed unmanned vehicle was given by Professor S. F. Singer, of the University of Maryland, and since this is well in accordance with the latest suggestions it is worth considering a little more closely.

Professor Singer's vehicle was named the "Minimum Orbit Unmanned Satellite, Earth," conveniently shortened to MOUSE. It was designed for upper-atmosphere research and for studies of the ultraviolet and X radiation coming from the Sun, which is unavailable to ground observers owing to the blocking-out effect of the air. It was to be a foot in diameter, carrying a total load of about 20 kilograms of scientific equipment, and was to circle the Earth at an altitude of something like 200 miles, so that it would have a revolution period of about 90 minutes. The orbit originally suggested was one which carried it over both poles, since a satellite traveling in such a path would be perpetually sunlit and would be capable of making a continuous record of solar activity.

Equatorial orbit   *Inclined orbit*

The vehicle as described by Professor Singer was to be shaped something like a barrel, the inside being filled with different types of scientific instruments, such as X-ray detectors, ultraviolet-radiation equipment, magnetometers, and radar beacons (it is really remarkable how much equipment can nowadays be packed into a small space). Naturally, these instruments would not last indefinitely owing to the problem of power supply, but solar power might well be pressed into service; the vehicle would experience no "night," and the supply of energy from the Sun would therefore be continuous, even though the technical difficulties of utilizing it would be considerable.

The polar orbit would not be the only possible one, and in fact the number of theoretical orbits is virtually limitless. Were the vehicle placed so as to move above the equator in an extended great circle, it would of course remain permanently over some part of the equator—but this orbit, though easy to visualize, has severe limitations. The curvature of the globe would prevent the satellite being observable at all except from a narrow belt to either side of the equator, and from the most densely populated regions of the Earth, such as the United States and Britain, it would never be seen at all. Here again there is an analogy with Phobos. The tiny Martian moon moves in an orbit not much inclined to the equatorial plane, and would never rise above the horizon in temperate or polar latitudes.

An orbit with its plane at 45 degrees inclination to the Earth's equator would give much greater scope. In this case the "subsatellite point," the point on the ground directly below the artificial moon, would appear like a wavy line if plotted on a terrestrial chart for each revolution. At various times the satellite would be directly over places as wide apart as Australia, South America, Africa, Spain, and Japan, so that full use could be made of it everywhere. Altogether, observations would be possible from anywhere on the Earth except beyond latitude 68 degrees north or south, which excludes only parts of Alaska, Greenland, Siberia and Antarctica. The ideal would be to have several MOUSE rockets (the abbreviation MICE seems inadmissible!) in various orbits; one polar, one equatorial, one at 45 degrees, and so on.

In a paper published in the *Journal* of the British Interplanetary Society in 1954, Professor Singer wrote that "within a few years, the means will be available to us for putting a vehicle such as the MOUSE into orbit." He has been proved right, and the satellite program now under way, known officially as "Project Vanguard," is in full accord with the statements that he made before the Eisenhower announcement. For instance, there will be at least ten satellites, all of them small, and most or all of them carrying instruments.

Clearly there is only one way to put a vehicle into free orbit: to convey it there by rocket, which means in effect by step rocket. With the liquid fuels available to us, no single-step arrangement is adequate. Frequent reference has been made to atomic power, and of course if the atom could be tapped it would make liquid fueling as obsolete as the steam car, but at the moment there is no immediate hope of any such thing.

Since the military operations over Hiroshima and Nagasaki which led to the abrupt end of the war in 1945, the world has been living in an "atomic age" in which the power of the atom has been brought home to us. It has been used for peaceful purposes as well as warlike ones, and atomic heating plants are already in operation. However, our knowledge is still very limited. We have only looked at the entrance to the powerhouse of the atom, and what lies within is still hidden from us. It is much easier to release atomic energy in one catastrophic burst by chain reaction, as in the various types of bomb, than to utilize the energy in dribs and drabs. Moreover, atomic devices require heavy shielding, so that the whole idea of an atomic rocket is still futuristic.

Many people who have gained their "knowledge" from sensational science-fiction magazines imagine that an atomic space craft would be quite different from a true rocket. This is not so. In any type of motor suitable for use in vacuum, the propulsion must be obtained by reaction, gases being emitted from the exhaust and so sending the body in the opposite direction; this is the principle of the man jumping off the truck, the skyrocket, and the liquid-fuel rocket. It is also the basis of any atomic device. Gas must be ejected; whether the energy to eject the gas is derived from gun-

If the satellite leaves the
coast of Florida at 12 noon . . .

by 2 P.M. it will have more
than circled the earth . . .

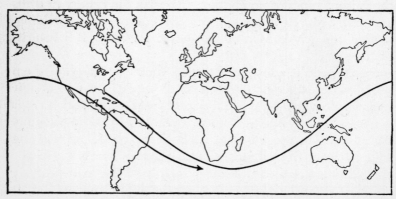

Two hours after takeoff the satellite will have made one trip
around the world and be on its way around the tip of Africa . . .

IN ONE AFTERNOON (NOON to 6 P.M.)

by 4 P.M. it will have nearly completed four round trips . . .

by 6 P.M. four times around while the Earth turned 90°.

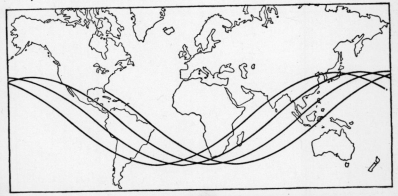

Six hours after takeoff the satellite has actually made four 360 degree turns, while the Earth has made one quarter turn.

powder, liquid oxygen and gasoline, or atomic power, the result is still a "rocket" in the proper sense of the term.

Papers have been written about atomic rockets, and many of these papers are theoretically sound, but theory and practice are two different things. So far as we ourselves are concerned, the atomic rocket is beyond our capabilities. In time it may be developed, and when that happens most of our worries about excess weight and mass will vanish, so that the step principle will be abandoned as an ancient and cumbersome arrangement. But that is looking far ahead, and it seems that the first ventures into space will be by means of rockets powered by liquid propellants.

We can now see why so much attention has been paid to the ideas put forward by men such as Goddard and Oberth. If we are to have a true space station, we must first have an unmanned orbital vehicle; if we are to have an unmanned orbital vehicle, we must first have an efficient liquid-fuel step rocket to launch it. Now that we have our rockets, we are ready to begin our real task.

CHAPTER 7

Project Vanguard

To BREAK free from the Earth's pull, a projectile would have to move at full escape velocity of 7 miles a second. However, a high-altitude orbital vehicle will make no attempt to escape completely, since it will merely fall into a closed orbit, so that the necessary speed is not so great.

Seven miles a second is equal to 25,000 miles per hour, far in excess of anything so far attained. "Orbital" velocity, however, is only 18,000 m.p.h. The extra 7,000 m.p.h. makes a great deal of difference.

If a vehicle can be set up beyond the limits of the resisting atmosphere, it will remain circling the Earth, and unless it is deliberately interfered with it will remain in a stable path. Nor will any power be needed to drive it along. There is an analogy here with the Earth; our world is in free fall around the Sun, but no artificial power is needed to push it round in its yearly journey.

Basically, therefore, the method of launching will be to raise the projectile to the required height and then give it a sideways thrust which will throw it into the right orbit.

The launching rocket will then have done its work, and can fall back into the atmosphere.

However, the actual procedure will be somewhat different. Always it is necessary to search for the most economical method of doing things; there can never be much fuel to spare. It is true that the upper steps of compound rockets have reached heights of well over 200 miles, but these rockets had only themselves to consider; they were not carrying much load, and near the top of their climb they had no energy reserves. A simple ascent is much easier than a planned launching.

"Project Vanguard" is a direct development of the Viking rocket program, which is itself a development of the research carried out on the V2. The experiments are scheduled to begin at the start of the International Geophysical Year, in July 1957, and details of what will be done are already known; the plans have been made public by Mr. Milton Rosen, Technical Director of the Project, and although they are bound to be subject to some alterations as the time draws near it is unlikely that they will be drastically changed.

The whole launcher will be a three-step arrangement, but at first sight it will seem simpler than this. The third and uppermost step, including the satellite itself, will be housed inside the nose of the second step, so that it will not be visible to the casual onlooker. There is a sound reason for this. The instrument-carrying satellite is comparatively fragile, and if exposed during the first rush through the dense atmosphere it would become violently heated, so that it would probably be harmed. When the second step has taken over, and is rising under its own power, the protecting cone will be jettisoned, as since most of the atmosphere will lie below there will no longer be any danger of damage to the satellite by overheating.

Let us now see just what will happen when the step rocket takes off. The bottom stage, which is essentially a very much improved Viking liquid-fuel rocket, will at first do all the work. It will take off vertically, but will then rise in a smooth curve, tilting gradually to the east (for reasons which will be described later). By the time it has risen to some 36 miles, it will be traveling at an angle of about 45 degrees to the vertical, it will then have exhausted its fuel, and will break away, dropping back to the ground and landing over two hundred miles away from its starting point.

The second step is another liquid-fuel rocket, and Mr. Rosen has described it as "the brain of the launching vehicle," since it contains the main controls that regulate the whole flight, timing the moments of ignition, cut-off, and the breaking away of the various stages. It will start firing immediately the bottom step falls away, and soon afterwards the protecting nose cone will be jettisoned, while the angle of curve of the orbit to the vertical will go on increasing. Firing will continue until the altitude has reached 140 miles, but when the second stage has exhausted its fuel it will not fall away at once in the manner of the bottom step; its speed will cause it to go on "coasting" upwards, just as a push-bicyclist who stops pedaling half-way up a hill will go on moving for some time before he comes to a halt.

Actually the coasting period will last for some time. The total distance covered will be 700 miles, and the final height about 300 miles above the ground, by which time the orbit will be more or less parallel with the Earth's surface. In other words, there is no real sideways kick; such a kick would use up far too much fuel. The direction is already correct by the time the second-third-stage combination has reached peak altitude, and all that has to be done is to eject the final step.

This step is an unguided (spin-stabilized) solid-propellant arrangement. It is to be fired away from the second stage at orbital height, and once the last separation has taken place no further control can be exercised; if there have been

STEPS IN LAUNCHING

SATELLITE

THIRD STAGE

SECOND STAGE

FIRST STAGE

1 *The three stage rocket is launched vertically. First stage lifts the rocket 36 miles in a gradual curve toward the horizontal. Second stage separates, and takes off under its own power.*

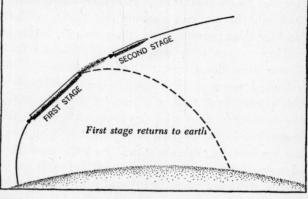

SECOND STAGE

FIRST STAGE

First stage returns to earth

2 *During second stage flight nose cone is ejected. At second stage burnout, rocket is 140 miles up and coasts to 300 miles altitude.*

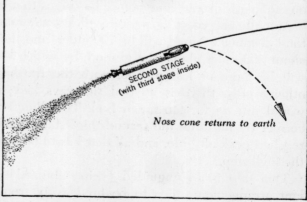

SECOND STAGE
(with third stage inside)

Nose cone returns to earth

← *Three stage satellite vehicle "Vanguard," 72 feet high; carries within its nose the 20 inch satellite sphere.*

THE SATELLITE INTO ORBIT

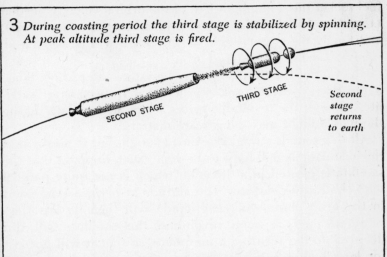

3 *During coasting period the third stage is stabilized by spinning. At peak altitude third stage is fired.*

SECOND STAGE

THIRD STAGE

Second stage returns to earth

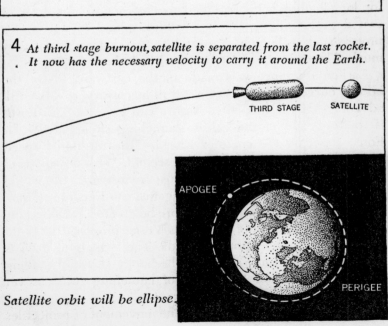

4 *At third stage burnout, satellite is separated from the last rocket. It now has the necessary velocity to carry it around the Earth.*

THIRD STAGE   SATELLITE

APOGEE

PERIGEE

Satellite orbit will be ellipse.

any mistakes, it will be too late to rectify them. The solid-fuel rocket provides about half of the orbital velocity needed (the other half has already been given by the second step), and finally the twenty-inch satellite itself will be separated, safely placed in its required orbit.

The fate of the third step may be rather interesting. Since it must reach orbital velocity, it too may become a "satellite," though the inevitable errors which accumulate during the whole flight may complicate matters.

All this sounds straightforward enough, but it means that the calculations will have to be very exact. Suppose that the satellite is ejected in a direction which is not quite parallel with the Earth's surface? The altitude at perigee (the point in the orbit closest to the ground) will then be less than required, and at each revolution the satellite will dip deeply into the resisting atmosphere, so that it will not last for long before being dragged to destruction. An error of two degrees might well be disastrous, and in a complex process such as launching a satellite two degrees is not very much. The correct velocity is equally vital.

Earlier, reference was made to the eastward tilt of the orbital curve. This is because it is necessary to take full advantage of the help that Nature can give us. The Earth is rotating, and at the chosen launching site—Patrick Air Force Base, on the coast of Florida—the rotational speed is over thirteen hundred feet per second. With an eastward tilt, this speed is made to help us; a westward tilt would mean that we would be fighting against the Earth's rotation, and the fuel needed would therefore be greater. Incidentally, it is interesting to note that Jules Verne proposed to build his wonderful space gun in Florida. The space gun itself is an impossibility; but Verne had the happy knack of making correct guesses, and his choice of launching site was yet another of them.

One of the uncertainties about the movement of projectiles

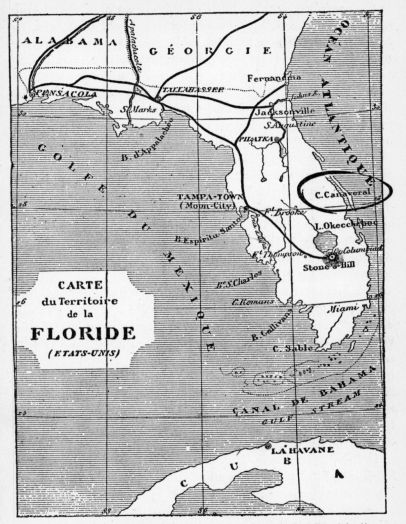

Map from Les Voyages Extraordinaires "De la Terre a la Lune" by Jules Verne.

First satellite will be launched at Cape Canaveral (circled), a little over a hundred miles from the fictional "Stone's-Hill" where Jules Verne's moon projectile began its flight of phantasy.

in the exosphere concerns the question of air densities at high altitudes, and this is a problem which could be solved by a simple missile just as well as by an instrument-carrying one. It is merely a case of watching its motion, and noting the "slowing down" effect caused by air resistance. If launched into a circular orbit at a height of 200 miles, the lifetime of a satellite would be just over a fortnight; at 300 miles, almost a year. But as we have seen, the actual orbits are not likely to be circular, so that only near perigee at each revolution will the satellite move inside the danger zone. Each time it plunges it will lose a little velocity, and as it falls gradually into denser and denser air it will spiral more quickly towards the ground until the frictional heat set up is sufficient to destroy the satellite. Of course, this will not apply if the perigee distance is still great enough to avoid the resisting atmosphere, and in this case the satellite will remain orbiting indefinitely.

The first instrument-carrying satellite will be about a foot and a half in diameter, with a total weight * of 21½ pounds. This may seem modest, but it is in fact sufficient for the vehicle to carry all sorts of instruments, ranging from cosmic ray detectors to radar beacons, and the information sent back to Earth will be of incalculable value. Before considering these points in more detail, however, it will be as well to try to answer one or two questions which are certain to be asked by everyone who takes a casual but intelligent interest in the project.

The first question is, of course: "Shall I be able to see the satellite? What will it look like—a basketball floating in the sky, or a brilliant disk, or just a faint speck of light?"

The nickname of "flying basketballs" which has been bestowed on the proposed satellites certainly does conjure up

---

* This means that the satellite will weigh 21½ pounds before it is launched. Once in free fall, the expression "weight" becomes totally meaningless, though the satellite's mass will be unaltered.

a picture of a large sphere hovering in the heavens apparently almost at roof-top height. Yet a moment's consideration will show that this idea is hopelessly wrong. A large modern aircraft is a massive structure with a vast wingspan, but when flying at an altitude of thousands of feet it does not look particularly impressive, and anyone who sees such an aircraft at close quarters for the first time must be impressed with the great dimensions. The satellite will be far smaller than such an aircraft, and will be much more distant, so that with the unaided eye (or even a telescope) it will not show a measurable disk. It will not even appear as bright as a conspicuous star. Under the best possible conditions, when it is near the overhead point in the late evening or early morning twilight, it may be just visible without optical aid as a faint point of light, and binoculars will show it easily.

The first of the satellites is to be launched in an orbit which will cover the area from 40 degrees north to 40 degrees south. This means that it will at times be visible from the United States. Later satellites may pass over higher latitudes than the first.

Secondly, the satellite will not shoot across the sky in the manner of a meteor. Here again there is an analogy with a high-flying, quick-moving aircraft. When a jet bomber is seen at an altitude of (say) 40,000 feet, it seems to be crawling, whereas the speed of a nearby insect is very noticeable. When near the overhead point, the satellite will take about half a second to move across an apparent width equal to the observed diameter of the Moon, so that although its motion will be perceptible it cannot possibly be mistaken for a shooting star. Obviously, studies of the position of the satellite will be most important, and amateur astronomers are expected to play a leading part.

There are some people who refuse to believe that a tiny body a mere foot and a half in diameter will be visible at all at a distance of over 200 miles. To show the error in this point of view, we must turn to astronomy. In late 1937 a small minor planet named Hermes approached to within half a million miles of the Earth, thereby causing sensational headlines in the press, but it was not a difficult telescopic object once one knew where to look for it, even though it was only about half a mile across. With my 12½-inch reflecting telescope I have picked up Phobos, the ten-mile moon of Mars, across a distance of forty million miles. There will thus be no difficulty in observing the "flying basketball."

At this point it may be of interest to mention the possibility of a natural earth satellite revolving round our globe at a distance less than that of the Moon. There is nothing theoretically impossible in the idea. There are myriads of meteors circling the Sun, and there is no hard and fast dividing line between a large meteor and a small minor planet; Hermes, for instance, might be placed in either category, and so might the object which devastated many square miles of Siberia when it landed there in 1908. Phobos and Deimos are hardly worthy of being called true Martian satellites, and a small body of similar size might well have fallen into an orbit round the Earth.

The idea was used by Jules Verne in his famous novel *Round the Moon*, probably the earliest true science-fiction story still widely read. Verne described the body graphically from the point of view of his heroes, who were on their way to the Moon in a hollow projectile fired from the mouth of a space-gun: "An enormous disk . . . it looked like a small moon reflecting the light of the large one. It advanced at a prodigious speed, and to the movement was added a movement of rotation on itself." The second satellite was in fact essential to Verne's story, since it was used to perturb the motion of the projectile and swing it into an orbit that carried it right around the Moon before returning it to the Earth.

The question was taken up in later years by the famous

American astronomer Professor W. H. Pickering, who wrote several papers on the subject between 1904 and 1922. He worked out that if the satellite revolved at a distance of 200 miles and had a diameter of one foot (note the similarity with the proposed vehicle of Project Vanguard) it should be easily visible with a small telescope, while a 10-foot body at 200 miles would be conspicuous without a telescope at all. Of course, such a body would have been detected long ago, and this is positive proof that if a second moon exists at all it must be distant and minute.

Pickering seems to have made a desultory search for such an object, but the question has been reopened recently by Dr. Clyde Tombaugh at the Lowell Observatory in Arizona. Few could be more fitted to the task, since Dr. Tombaugh first achieved fame in 1930 by detecting the long-sought ninth planet, Pluto. So far he has been unsuccessful, and it is safe to say that if another satellite exists it can be nothing more than a lump of rock a few yards across circling us at a great distance. Nor is it possible for a satellite to exist in an orbit which keeps it permanently behind the Moon, and thus invisible from Earth. The latter idea is revived every now and then, but is scientifically absurd. [Incidentally, there were recent reports that an American astronomer had discovered a whole swarm of minor planets in orbit round the Earth. I have been unable to find out how this rumor arose, but it is completely unfounded.] It seems, therefore, that the satellites of Project Vanguard are not likely to have natural rivals.

At the time of the Eisenhower announcement, the International Astronautical Federation was about to meet in Copenhagen. All the world's leading interplanetary societies were taking part, and for the first time the Russians were represented. Undoubtedly there has been great astronautical interest in the Soviet Union, and here is a chance for scientists of East and West to join in friendly co-operation.

Britain's part in the Geophysical Year program will be concerned mainly with the rocket exploration of high altitudes. It is not so far planned to launch a British satellite, but preparations for rocket investigations are well under way. We hope to learn much about such phenomena as ionospheric winds, the high-temperature layer, and the airglow.

The airglow, or faint luminosity of the sky, is still not properly understood. At night it contributes about two-fifths of the total light of the sky, and is distinct from scattering of starlight; it originates in the atmosphere itself. It is a lofty phenomenon, so that it is far beyond the reach of aircraft or balloons, and until very recently little had been done in this field of research. Probably the airglow is due to ultraviolet radiation from the Sun acting upon certain atoms in the upper air and exciting them to luminosity. Some of the atoms so affected may be of sodium, and if sodium vapor is released at a height of (say) 60 miles, the top of the chemosphere, we can learn a good deal more about the airglow and associated phenomena. The experimentally released sodium will disperse after a while and will merge with the natural atmospheric sodium, which is probably present as a result of salt being carried upwards from the sea. The effects of such a sodium release are mildly spectacular, though comparatively brief. An equally interesting experiment was carried out in 1956, when an Aerobee rocket loaded with nitric oxygen gas under high pressure was sent up to 60 miles from the Holloman Air Development Center in New Mexico. When the gas was released, during the hours of darkness, ground observers saw what looked like a bright star, which grew in size until it was four times as large as the full Moon and about half as bright, before spreading out and fading into invisibility. Obviously, much valuable information about the upper air can be gained from experiments of this sort.

One matter needing attention is that of wind speeds in

the stratosphere and ionosphere. It is easy to talk about a "200 knot gale" at 60 miles up, but it must be remembered that at this height the pressure is less than 0.001 mm. of mercury, so that the atmospheric density is comparable with a laboratory "vacuum" and the so-called gale has very little force. Release of fine smoke particles is one way of obtaining more reliable information, and this too must be done by means of rockets.

Yet another method is to make use of sound waves. An explosion at high altitude must take some time to reach the ground, whereas the time taken by the flash to reach ground observers can be disregarded, since light travels at 186,000 miles per second. It has been proposed to fire grenades from rockets at various altitudes. The time-lag between the appearance of the flash and the detection of the sound will therefore give positive information about the pressures and temperatures in the upper strata.

These experiments, like the satellite programs themselves, will certainly not be confined to any one nation. The United States leads the way, but so long as all the information is pooled it makes little difference whether the researchers come from London, Moscow, or New York. There are no frontiers in space.

The international aspect of pure science!

CHAPTER 8

Research with Unmanned Satellites

THE COST of Project Vanguard will be enormous. On March 20, 1956, the House of Representatives approved the spending of over $19 million on the program scheduled for the International Geophysical Year alone, and this is rather too much to throw away upon a project that is of dubious value. Fortunately, however, there can be no doubt about the value of the program now under way; it is $19 million well spent.

The motions of the satellites will of course be of the greatest interest. If they deviate from their calculated paths, it should be possible to find out why. Since every known perturbation will be allowed for, the straying of the satellites should help astronomers to improve their theories—remembering that once a satellite is in free orbit, it has become a true astronomical body bound by the usual laws of planetary motion.

The working-out of the orbit will not be the simple business that so many people imagine. The position of the true Moon will affect the satellite, since the Moon revolves round the Earth once a month and is not always at just the same distance from us (221,600 miles at minimum and 252,950 at maximum). Nor is the Earth's distance from the Sun constant, owing to the slight but appreciable eccentricity of the terrestrial orbit. Actually the Sun's influence on the natural Moon is greater than the Earth's, and the solar pull on the artificial satellite will also have to be taken into account. Further complications are introduced by the fact that the Earth itself is not regular in form. There is an equatorial bulge, and this too will have a major effect on the satellite's motion. It is hardly surprising that the mathematical astronomer cannot hope for absolute precision, and direct observations of the satellite will be of great help.

When the satellite passes into the shadow of the Earth, it will naturally suffer "eclipse" as direct sunlight is cut off from it. The Moon is periodically eclipsed in this way, and when the shadow of our world falls across it the Moon would disappear altogether but for the bending or refraction of light in the higher reaches of the Earth's air. (On several occasions the Moon has in fact vanished, as in 1761, when the Swedish astronomer Per Wargentin stated that for half an hour it could not be found even with a telescope. All lunar eclipses are not equally "dark," but the variations are due to different conditions in the upper air and have no connection with the Moon itself.) However, the eclipsed satellite will be trackable by radar, even at night. We have even managed to obtain radar echoes from the Moon, so that there will be no trouble in following a body a mere couple of hundred miles distant.

Another use for the satellite will be as a navigational aid. All wartime navigators, both air and naval, will remember the method by which observation of the apparent position of a star or planet enables the observer to draw a position-line on his map, somewhere along which he must lie. The fast-moving satellite, passing from horizon to horizon in less than half an hour, will be a most welcome addition to the heavens.

All these investigations can be carried out by using a simple satellite which carries no instruments. When we turn to more complex problems, instrument-bearing projectiles are needed. If all goes well, such projectiles should be in orbit by the end of the geophysical year (July 1958), and to the physicist, the chemist and the astronomer their value will be inestimable.

Let us return for a moment to the obscuring effect of the atmosphere. The human eye responds to wavelengths of between 4,000 and 7,500 angströms, which is what we call "visible light," and the optical window extends from 2,900 to 30,000 angströms. The shorter ultraviolet and X-rays coming from the Sun are thus unobservable, since their wavelengths are less than 2,900 angströms; even near the point of "block-out" studies are difficult.

The first attempt to record the Sun's ultraviolet spectrum was made by E. and V. Regener in 1934. In those days rockets were still in their infancy, and the Regeners used a balloon, which was launched from Stuttgart and went up to 19½ miles. The solar spectrum was recorded down to 2,875 angströms, and further work of similar nature was undertaken by American balloonists in the following year, but it was obvious that altitudes of only 20 to 30 miles were of little real use. To record radiation of 2,000 angströms it is necessary to go up to about 40 miles, and radiation of 1,500 angströms involves an ascent to 60 miles. This is beyond any device but the rocket.

At the end of the war, numbers of unused V2s were taken to the United States to be employed in scientific research. On June 28, 1946, a V2 was sent up to nearly 70 miles, equipped with a spectrograph. Unfortunately it came down nose-first and buried itself in the desert, completely destroying the film, so that it will never be known whether the actual experiment was successful or not. On October 10 another V2 reached over 100 miles, and this time the film was not destroyed; it showed spectra down to 2,100 angströms. As a matter of fact the only successful exposures during this ascent were made well below peak height of the climb, but they were enough to show that the method was perfectly sound. More recently, photographs have been obtained down to as far as 977 angströms.

However, researches with normal rockets can never be very satisfactory. They cannot be prolonged, and there is always the risk that the films will be destroyed during the journey back to Earth. This latter trouble applies with equal force to the unmanned satellite, but in all other respects the orbital vehicle is vastly superior. Not only will it be more stable, but it will enable us to make exposures extending over many hours instead of two or three minutes. A polar orbit will even allow a continuous record of the ultraviolet sent out by the Sun. The information picked up by instruments in the satellite can be conveyed to the ground by radio telemetering techniques, so that actual recovery of the film is not essential.

Power supply in the satellite will naturally be a major problem. Even if solar power can be used to some extent, the technical difficulties are considerable. In the first vehicles, it seems that power supplies will consist of normal batteries, and the instruments will not be kept "turned on" all the whole time; they must come into operation whenever the satellite is suitably placed for observation from a ground station, as they must conserve their power. Automatic timing is virtually impossible, so that the instruments will have to be turned on by remote control from the ground, while a mechanical device in the satellite itself will turn the equipment off again after a set period.

This study of solar ultraviolet is important in many ways. The varying emission has, for instance, a marked effect on radio communications, as every short-wave amateur knows. The radio-reflecting layers in the upper air are indeed produced by the Sun's ultraviolet, and if we could find out more about the processes going on in the Sun itself we might be able to do something about the perennial problem of radio fading.

To the visual astronomer observing the Sun directly with the aid of a telescope,* there seems to be little activity going on. There are frequent outbreaks of dark spots, and these spots reach a numerical maximum every eleven years or so; they can be followed as they are carried slowly across the disk by the Sun's rotation. Little else can be seen, apart from brighter patches (faculæ) which are generally, though not invariably, associated with spot-groups. The rest of the disk appears uniform enough, and the Sun is a stable star. This is fortunate for us, since even a minor alteration in the output of light and heat would affect our climates. It is probable that the periodical ice ages which have occurred throughout the Earth's history have in fact been due to such a cause.

However, this stability does not extend to the emission of ultraviolet. This radiation originates in the Sun's atmosphere, about which our knowledge is still rather scanty, and its importance to the astronomer is obvious. It sometimes happens that a small bright filament on the disk will grow and increase in brilliancy until what is known as a "flare" develops, and the appearance of a flare is always accompanied by a sudden increase in ultraviolet emission. This naturally affects the radio reflecting layers in the upper air, and radio fading results. A few hours later, effects upon the compass needle are observed in the form of a so-called magnetic storm.

Solar flares are only rarely visible by direct observation,

---

* The Sun should always be observed by projecting the disk on to a screen. Direct observation through a telescope is dangerous, even when a dark glass is used, and may result in permanent damage to the eye.

HOW SOLAR ACTIVITY AFFECTS RADIO

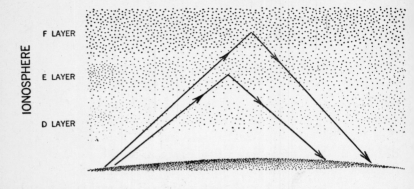

Long distance radio communi-cation takes place because radio waves are reflected by layers of the Ionosphere, as shown in the above diagram.

During the period of intense solar activity, illustrated by this solar "prominence" (left) ...

... The "D" layer of Ionosphere becomes intensely ionized. Radio waves are absorbed; "fading" results. (below)

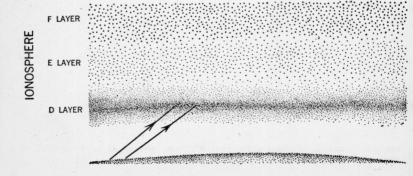

and special instruments are needed to detect them. Nor can they be predicted, and as they are very short-lived many of them must pass by without being noticed at all. Studies of ultraviolet emission must result in their being better understood, and until the artificial satellite is available we are working under a great handicap.

It may be added that one of the most interesting solar outbursts of recent years took place on February 23, 1956, at about 3.45 hours Greenwich Mean Time. Short-wave radio was dislocated, and for some time telephone conversations between London and New York became impossible; there was also a tremendous increase in cosmic-ray intensity, which rose temporarily to twice its normal value. Compared with an outburst of this nature, a hydrogen bomb becomes as puny as a firefly compared with a searchlight.

Magnetic storms and associated phenomena such as auroræ (polar lights) are associated not only with ultraviolet, but with streams of electrified particles sent out by the Sun. The emission of these particles also increases at the time of a flare; the time lag between the flare itself and the magnetic storm is due to the fact that the particles take hours to cover the 93-million-mile gap between Earth and Sun, whereas the ultraviolet light does the journey in only eight minutes. Here again, instruments set up in the satellite will help us to learn more about these streams of particles. We may expect to unravel some of the many mysteries that still surround magnetism in general and to study the magnetic fields which exist in the upper regions of the Earth's atmosphere.

As well as protecting us from ultraviolet, the atmosphere also serves as a shield against the extremely penetrative cosmic rays. These rays do not come from the Sun, but have their origin in deep space. It used to be thought that they were merely short-wave radiations, but this view has been shown to be incorrect. Strictly speaking they are not rays at all, but streams of particles made up chiefly of protons and the nuclei of various heavier atoms.

All matter is made up of atoms, which collect into atom-groups or molecules. There are comparatively few types of atoms, and from these types all matter in the universe is built up. The total number known to occur naturally is only 92, and each type has its own characteristics. These elements form a complete series from number 1 (hydrogen) to 92 (uranium), and there are no gaps left in the sequence.

It is not easy to give a good general picture of an atom. The old idea was to describe it as a sort of miniature solar system, with a central nucleus around which revolved particles known as electrons. The "atomic number" of the element then depended upon the number of planetary electrons, hydrogen having 1, helium 2, lithium 3 and so on, up to the 92 of uranium. It was also stated that various causes could lead to an atom being ionized, or deprived of some of its electrons. Normal helium has two planetary electrons; when singly ionized it has only one, and is thus incomplete, while doubly ionized helium has no electrons at all.

Actually this picture is not correct. To go into a proper explanation is impossible in a few lines, but at least the general idea as given above is not entirely misleading, particularly with regard to ionization.

It has been found that the cosmic rays consist of high-speed atomic nuclei stripped of their electrons. The main or primary rays include comparatively massive nuclei, such as those of iron (atomic number 36) and even tin (50). Moving at their colossal speeds these primaries have great powers of penetration, and it is possible that they will harm living tissue. But for the shielding atmosphere, life on the Earth could not have developed along its present lines.

Fortunately for us the heavy primaries, which are the dangerous members of the cosmic ray family, smash into the upper atmosphere and collide with air molecules, shattering both molecules and themselves and producing "secondary" fragments. These secondaries collide in their turn, and often a whole series of collisions takes place, so that only sub-secondary radiations reach the ground. Needless to say, these are harmless.

The primaries are first encountered at slightly below 50,000 feet, and the ionizing effects seem to be greatest at about 17 miles. This was found by balloon experiments as long ago as 1910. Recent rocket experiments have extended the observable range, and it has been found that above 35 miles there is no further change in cosmic-ray intensity, so that so far as the rays are concerned we can regard 35 miles as being the top of the atmosphere.

Manned aircraft have risen far above 50,000 feet, and monkeys and mice have been sent beyond the 35-mile limit. No ill effects have been observed, and we know therefore that cosmic radiation is not immediately lethal. On the other hand, our knowledge of the whole phenomenon is extremely sketchy, mainly because we have so far been unable to study the primaries except for periods of a few minutes at a time when the instrument-carrying rockets have entered the main zone. The problem is an urgent one, since if we are going to develop high-altitude airplanes we must find out just what effects the cosmic rays have.

The advantages of the unmanned satellite are very clear. Detectors can be exposed to the full cosmic-ray barrage for as long as is desired, and information sent back to the ground. In this way it should be possible to learn enough to determine the origin of the rays, which is at present unknown—despite the many plausible-sounding theories that have been advanced from time to time.

Even the relatively massive "heavy primaries" are, of course, inconceivably minute judged by normal standards, but there are many larger bodies to be met with in space. During a rich meteor shower, it is possible to see several

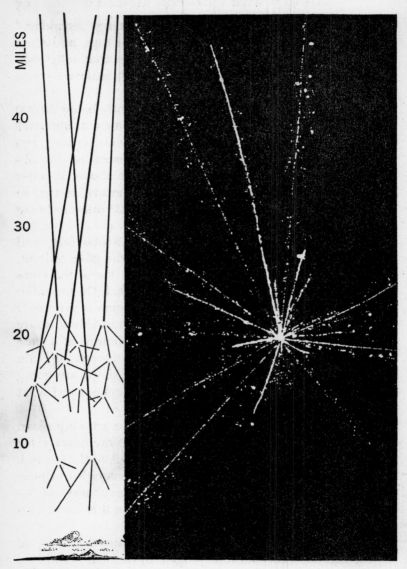

The atmosphere forms a shield against cosmic rays. Heavy "primaries" collide with air molecules, form "secondaries." Photo (right) shows track of cosmic rays on photo emulsion.

hundreds of shooting-stars per hour; even when no major shower is in progress the watchful observer will be able to detect meteors in plenty. One of the classical objections to flight beyond the atmosphere is that "any projectile flying higher than fifty miles will be broken up by meteoric bombardment." The flaw in this argument is that most meteors are extremely small, the large members of the swarms being vanishingly scarce.

We can disregard the occasional giants which plunge earthwards and produce sizeable craters. The only example during the present century has been the Siberian Meteorite of 1908. During each 24-hour period, it has been estimated that less than a dozen meteorites reach ground level. About five million meteors a tenth of an inch or so in diameter enter the air in an equivalent period, and the largest of these account for the visible shooting stars. On the other hand, the number of smaller particles is stupendous. About 750,-000,000,000,000,000 meteors in all are trapped by the Earth daily, so that out in space they must be very common. The majority are far inferior to grains of dust, and have been aptly christened "micrometeorites."

Since micrometeorites are too small to cause shooting-star effects, it is impossible to study them from beneath the atmosphere. Once again it was found that rockets could help. Smooth metal plates were attached to V2s and other projectiles, and after the flights microscopic examination revealed small pits in the plates which could be due only to micrometeorites. It was also possible to use more complex methods of detection while the ascent was in progress. Results showed that each square foot of material is likely to be struck by a micrometeorite every two seconds, but fortunately the tiny mass of each particle means that it is not dangerous.

The origin of meteors is still unknown, and we are more likely to solve the problem by studying micrometeorites than by concentrating upon the spectacular but rare giants. So far as we can tell, the artificial satellite is the only way to do so with real success.

These are but a few of many uses to which the man-made moon will be put. We live upon a small and insignificant planet; if we are to probe the secrets of the greater universe we must do our best to break free, as otherwise we are in much the position of an artist who is content to sit behind a frosted glass window while he paints the landscape beyond. The practical advantages of the satellite will be many, but whatever happens we shall be gathering knowledge— and desire for knowledge is still the greatest virtue of the human race.

CHAPTER 9

Satellites as Military Weapons

TWENTY years ago, the science of rocketry was still in its
early stages. The liquid-fuel arrangements of Goddard and
the Raketenflugplatz workers were not much more powerful
than skyrockets, and very few scientists believed that flight
beyond the stratosphere was at all possible.

Progress during the last two decades has therefore been
amazingly rapid. Much of it has come as a result of the work
carried out at Peenemünde. Yet Peenemünde was a scientific
research station only because it had to be so; its chief purpose was to develop a weapon for mass destruction.

It is a pity that so many scientific inventions have been
adapted for use in war. Gunpowder is one example; the
internal-combustion engine another; the airplane yet another; and the rocket a fourth. As was mentioned, we have
records of a rocket barrage used as far back as the thirteenth
century, and a hundred and fifty years ago the British Army
possessed a full-scale rocket mounted corps. The fact that
the war rocket was not subsequently used much until
Peenemünde was simply because it was not reliable enough,

and mass slaughter could better be accomplished by means
of normal artillery.

Political leaders were not at all interested in the space-
flight ideas of men like Oberth, and even Goddard's high-
altitude research failed to arouse much official enthusiasm.
Rocket development was always hampered by lack of money.
Untold millions of dollars, pounds, and marks were squan-
dered on defense programs and improved military devices,
but there was never any to spare for pure science. Goddard
himself was handicapped by financial troubles, and the
break-up of the German VfR was due largely to the same
cause.

So matters would have drifted on but for the sharpness
of the German Command. When the Nazis came to power
and began preparing for the coming war, some of their
leaders realized that the liquid-fuel rockets of the Raketenflugplatz could be turned into devastating weapons. Peenemünde was created, and work on rocketry began in earnest.
It is true that Dornberger and his staff were not provided
with the money and priority they really needed, but at least
they had enough financial backing to allow them to carry
on experiments on a scale far larger than anything attempted
before.

It must be admitted that only military considerations could
have forced so much money out of any Government. It must
also be admitted that it would be unjust to put the whole
blame for the war rocket upon Germany. The fact that other
nations did not follow suit was due only to the fact that they
did not realize just what the rocket could do. Had Allied
leaders been equally alert, they would certainly have created
a Peenemünde of their own.

The V2 was probably the deadliest of all weapons up to
the time of the atom bomb, and a V2-type rocket fitted with
an atomic warhead is a terrifying prospect. If used on a
large scale, it might indeed depopulate the Earth. But the

original use of the V2 as a weapon was Hitler's doing, not von Braun's.

In a 1954 speech made on (appropriately) April 1, the Rt. Hon. C. R. Attlee said in Parliament that "with us, the danger comes from the scientists." This is ridiculous, since the task of the scientist is to gather as much knowledge as he can, and he is not to be held responsible for the subsequent misuse of it by political leaders. If proof of this were needed, it is surely provided by the case of von Braun himself, who was actually arrested by the German Gestapo at a crucial stage of the Peenemünde work because, it was alleged, he was too interested in space flight and too little interested in war. Von Braun did more than anyone else to develop the V2, yet for years now he has been a valued and most welcome Honorary Member of the British Interplanetary Society. Further comment is unnecessary.

Actually the first extraterrestrial weapon to be proposed was the "space mirror," about which a good deal was heard after the end of the war. It was said that German scientists had planned to build a great orbital mirror which could focus the Sun's rays upon a small area of the Earth, such as a city, and burn it up. Theoretically the idea is sound enough, and Oberth himself once wrote that such a mirror could "burn cities, explode ammunition plants, and do damage to the enemy generally."

Needless to say, the space mirror never even reached the blueprint stage. There are so many practical disadvantages to the whole idea that there is not the slightest chance of the mirror being built. It reminds one of an incredible scheme proposed by a Frenchman, Charles Cros, as long ago as 1869. Cros was firmly convinced that Mars is inhabited, and in order to get in touch with the "Martians" he proposed to build a vast mirror in the Sahara Desert, curved so that it would focus the solar rays upon the Martian deserts and scorch the sand there. By judicious swinging of the mirror, it would thus be possible to write words on the surface of the Red Planet. Exactly what words it was proposed to transmit he did not reveal.

The efficiency of the military rocket has been proved; the space mirror and similar devices can be rejected as unworkable. There remains the problem of the orbital satellite. Can it, too, be adapted for warlike purposes?

Fortunately the answer seems to be a rather decisive "no." An unmanned satellite would, of course, be a valuable observation point, since it could swing over both friendly and enemy territories; from a manned artificial moon no secrets could be hidden, and Iron Curtains would promptly melt. There have been reports that the U.S. Air Force is considering such a reconnaissance vehicle, called "Big Brother." On the other hand, it is unlikely that the crew of a satellite could undertake precision bombing with atomic missiles, and still more unlikely that any such thing would be attempted, since the atomic high-altitude rocket—the improved V2—would by itself be sufficient to destroy both attacker and attacked.

There are signs that world statesmen are at last starting to realize the full danger of a third war. One of the most encouraging features of the American satellite program is that it is to be truly international, with results made available to the scientists of all countries. Let us trust that this is the beginning of a saner era.

The artificial satellite, therefore, will probably not be used as a military base, and it is pointless to enter into a discussion as to whether or not it would be easy prey for a guided missile. It is to be hoped that instead of being regarded as a potential menace, the satellite—when it is set up —will be looked upon as a symbol that Man is at last beginning to conquer himself.

CHAPTER 10

Manned Satellites

UP TO NOW we have been dealing principally with hard facts. Rockets are already well developed, liquid-fuel motors have proved their worth, step rockets have been fired with success, and instrument-carrying rockets have penetrated far into the exosphere, where there is so little air left that to all intents and purposes it can be disregarded. Moreover, the unmanned satellite has been planned in detail, and may be in orbit by the end of 1957—in fact several satellites should have been launched by then, some of which will bear scientific equipment.

However, we cannot yet go much farther without drawing upon our imagination. The present and following chapters of this book must be regarded purely as scientific speculation. There is no harm in discussing space stations, interplanetary rockets and flights to the Moon; such ideas are not fantastic, as they were a mere twenty years ago. On the other hand, neither are they within our grasp. There has been many an "artist's conception" of a manned space station. One of these is shown on pages 104 and 105; it needs no further

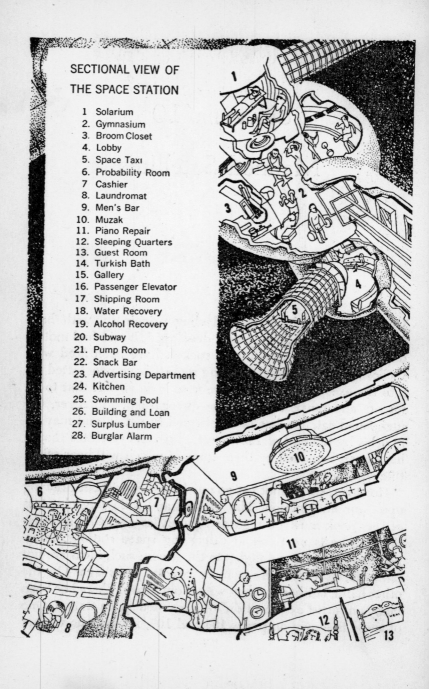

SECTIONAL VIEW OF
THE SPACE STATION

1. Solarium
2. Gymnasium
3. Broom Closet
4. Lobby
5. Space Taxi
6. Probability Room
7. Cashier
8. Laundromat
9. Men's Bar
10. Muzak
11. Piano Repair
12. Sleeping Quarters
13. Guest Room
14. Turkish Bath
15. Gallery
16. Passenger Elevator
17. Shipping Room
18. Water Recovery
19. Alcohol Recovery
20. Subway
21. Pump Room
22. Snack Bar
23. Advertising Department
24. Kitchen
25. Swimming Pool
26. Building and Loan
27. Surplus Lumber
28. Burglar Alarm

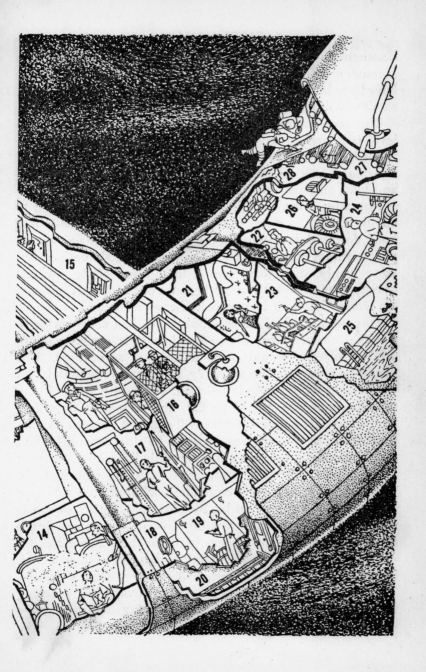

comment here. No man has yet risen to a height of more than seventeen miles, and even rocket-borne animals and insects have been limited to the lower ionosphere, so that the manned satellite still lies a long way in the future.

The acceleration as a manned rocket rises from ground level is bound to be violent, even when the step principle is used, and will strain the human body severely. Physical movement will be impossible owing to the increased "g," and blast-off must therefore be automatic.

Normal gravity, or "1g," is the pull we are accustomed to on the Earth's surface; it is sufficient to pull a free-falling body downwards with an acceleration of 32 feet per second per second. A man who moved upwards with similar acceleration would, of course, feel a total force of 2g—normal gravity plus an equal amount because of his upward motion. He would therefore feel twice as heavy as normal.

This would be bad enough, but the violent acceleration of a rocket shortly after blast-off, when it is working up to orbital velocity, would cause a force of several g's. This would be most unpleasant. At 7g, for instance, human blood would seem as heavy as liquid iron. The best way for a man to resist increased g is to lie flat, but even then there is a limit to what the human frame will stand; if the acceleration becomes too great, the results must be disastrous. The first stages of a flight into space will certainly be painful.

We cannot tell when the manned satellite will be built. Various estimates have been made; von Braun has said that in his view it may be in orbit by 1963, while other scientists have denied that it can ever be constructed. As usual, the truth probably lies somewhere between these two extremes.

When a proper manned satellite has been constructed, however, flights to the Moon will follow within a decade. The two main difficulties of a lunar voyage are escaping from the Earth's atmosphere and learning how to survive

> *"Quite likely the most effective flying machine would be one carried by a vast number of little birds."*
> S. Newcomb

in vacuo. Once the manned satellite has been built, both these vital problems will, of course, have been solved.

There are still pessimists who ridicule the whole idea of space flight, just as an eminent American astronomer, Simon Newcomb, ridiculed the heavier-than-air machine only a few years before the Wright brothers made their first clumsy "hops." A different view has been expressed by Sir Harold Spencer Jones, Astronomer Royal until the end of 1955, who wrote: "To conquer space would be an achievement surpassing anything that man has yet accomplished; the greater therefore is the challenge. There are those who are prepared to accept the challenge, and who can say that they will not succeed? . . . Their faith is not mere idle fancy, but there are solid grounds for believing that sooner or later success will be theirs."

We have, therefore, every right to speculate, and let us begin with the means by which a manned satellite may be constructed.

It will have to be much farther from the Earth than a mere
200 miles. There are several reasons for this, one being that
a manned station will have to be well clear of the limits of
air resistance. Another reason is that the pull of the Earth
itself might lead to the disruption of a complex satellite
relatively close to the surface.* In his original calculations, Oberth suggested a distance of 600 miles; recent
research has increased this somewhat, and the distance
favored by von Braun, who has planned his space station
in great detail, is 1,075 miles. This would mean a periodic
time of two hours instead of only 90 minutes.

Actually, the extra distance does not involve any major
additional problems. The chief difficulty of rising above
the atmosphere lies in reaching orbital velocity; once this
has been done, the rocket can reach a thousand miles almost
as easily as it can attain two hundred. This can be brought
home by a simple example. Consider two rockets, one starting at two miles a second and the other at three. The first
rocket will rise only to 350 miles before it drops back, but
the second will reach 900 miles, showing that a comparatively
small increase in the starting speed makes a great deal of
difference in the final reckoning.

Small unmanned satellites will, of course, be built in terrestrial laboratories, and will be sent into orbit by means of
a step-rocket launcher. This procedure cannot be followed
in the case of a manned vehicle, which must be far larger
and more massive. To construct such a vehicle on the surface
of the Earth and then try to convey it above the atmosphere
would be about as practicable as building the roof of a factory
in one piece and then jacking it up on to the tops of the walls.
If the manned satellite is to be set up at all, it must be built
in small sections and assembled out in space.

* This is a highly technical problem, and one which has not yet been
properly solved. Experience with unmanned satellites is the only real way
to find the answer.

Reduced to its simplest terms, the procedure must then be to construct each section separately and send it up into the same orbit a thousand miles above the ground. The idea sounds absurd, but is not actually so. Two sections in the same orbit will be at relative rest, just as two ants on the rim of a car-wheel are at relative rest even when the wheel is rotating around its hub. They will not drift apart, but will remain circling the Earth until ready to be used.

Each section will have to be sent up by step rocket, which will make the whole venture extremely expensive even if the lower steps can be recovered and used more than once. At first, the orbit-reaching steps of the rockets themselves will be used for building, which has led Arthur C. Clarke to invent the graphic term "cannibalization." As the project gathers momentum, relays of rockets will climb up into the selected orbit and "dump" their payloads. The first men to arrive will either base themselves in their own rockets, or will construct a spherical pressurized chamber to serve as a headquarters. The space station will then be put together gradually.

Since all the various pieces will be circling the Earth in free fall, conditions of zero gravity will prevail—which will be a great help. On the other hand, it is wrong to suppose that a man could take hold of an iron girder and swing it about as easily as a feather. Despite the absence of conventional "weight," the girder will still retain its mass and its inertia.

The space station can be assembled only by human agency, and this will mean that the crew must leave the safety of their rockets and go outside in suitable vacuum equipment. Once again, the popular idea of a "space suit," with its perfect flexibility, its comfort and its fishbowl helmet, is very wide of the mark. To begin with, the suit must be perfectly pressurized in order to avoid the danger of blood boiling, and this means that it must be rigid, probably with mechanically

MEN'S FASHIONS for...

  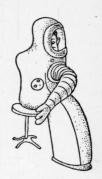

HIGH ALTITUDE SPACE SUITS above are real...all others on these two pages are imaginary. Left to right: Wiley Post's 1935 "stratosphere suit" used in actual flight up to 8 miles; U. S. Navy 1953 full-pressure flight suit for use up to 13 miles; U. S. Air Force contemporary one-arm experimental suit.

1928
German

1936
Russian

1952
American

Metal tubing and quilted chest protector no longer are in style.

Dumpy, lumpy look typical of most Soviet fashions.

Designed by famous space artist. Shows superior-cut and finish.

THE FLEXIBLE SPACE SUIT. Though impractical for operation in space, they show considerable variation in style appeal.

....travel in space

Deluxe 1952 rigid suit by Oberth

Radiator for cooling suit

Entrance

Rear view mirror

Telephone plug

Transition period from form-fitting to rigid suit.

THE RIGID SPACE SUIT *sacrifices the casual look, but is the most practical suit for everyday wear.*

Magnets

Von Braun's non-humanoid space suit with remote control arms.

Non-humanoid robot, in humanoid suit, from the motion picture "Forbidden Planet."

controlled arms and legs. The transparent section of the helmet will be narrow, giving a restricted field of view, in order to minimize the risks to the eyes of ultraviolet radiation; all communication must be by radio, since sound waves are carried by air and there is no air in outer space.

Temperature control provides yet more problems. The "bitter cold of space" so often referred to by fiction writers is a myth, since space is virtually nothingness and can have no temperature at all. A material body in space will, of course, have a definite temperature, and in general the sunward side of such a body will be too hot, while the shadowed side will be too cold. There are many ways of controlling temperature, and quite often the aim will be to lose heat rather than to gain it, but altogether the space suit is not the simple outfit that most people imagine.

Partial pressure suits have been developed for the use of airmen flying above the 63,000 feet limit, not for actual use in normal flights but as a safeguard against unexpected loss of pressure in the cabin. Research is going on all the time, but so far no completely efficient vacuum suit has been made, and this must, of course, be done before we can ever consider building a manned satellite.

A space-clad man in the same orbit as the satellite would neither drift away nor fall back to the ground, since he would be sharing in the satellite's motion and would be just another ant on the wheel rim; but we must not be overoptimistic —much remains to be done. At present there is little point in discussing engineering problems connected with assembling the satellite, but it may be of interest to say something about the form it is likely to take.

Various designs have been drawn up. The most complete is that of von Braun, who plans to make his station wheel-shaped. On this design the total diameter will be 250 feet, with the outer rim—which contains the living quarters—30 feet across. There is a good reason for this. Journeys to and from the station will be difficult and expensive, so that they will be cut to a minimum and the crew members will have to stay out in space for months on end. Although it is believed that zero gravity is not harmful when experienced for short periods, there is a chance that it may endanger the health of men who endure it consistently; there is no substitute for true gravity, but a slow rotation of the space wheel would provide synthetic gravity in the outer rim in the form of centrifugal force.

All suggested designs therefore allow for rotation, and so far there is little to choose between them. We can no more decide upon a set pattern than Orville Wright could have planned the details of a jet stratoplane when he first left the ground at Kitty Hawk. For the moment, however, von Braun's wheel is a reasonable guess.

When finally set in orbit, the manned satellite will prove invaluable to every branch of science. It should, for instance, enable us to make really accurate weather forecasts, which is beyond us at the moment. To predict future conditions, the meteorologist has to know the present state of things with regard to temperature, wind, humidity, pressure and cloud formation, not only for his own area but for the entire planet. At the moment he has to depend upon reports sent in from weather stations, and these are bound to be incomplete, partly because the stations are too few in number and partly because some regions of meteorological importance (such as the Poles) have no stations at all. It is therefore out of the question to make a reliable forecast for more than a few hours ahead, and even over short periods the conditions may alter quickly enough to make the forecast utterly wrong.

From a satellite, particularly one set in the 45-degree orbit, the forecaster would have a "bird's-eye view" of the whole Earth, and as the satellite swung around in its two-hour orbit he would be able to see everything he wanted. Whole meteorological systems would be spread out for his inspection, and although he would still have to depend upon ground stations to some extent it would not be long before the behavior of the atmosphere became really understood. It might even be possible to predict long-range climate for various latitude zones of the Earth and for various seasons.

It is always convenient to know whether it is likely to be wet or dry, but to the farmer and the agriculturalist a definite knowledge of what to expect would be a boon indeed. The short-period forecast is not of much use in the long run, but once it becomes possible to predict the weather for some time ahead the task of those who grow our food will be much lightened. We can hardly hope to gain such knowledge except by observation from a satellite.

Astronomy will benefit equally. The blocking-out effect of the upper air has already been discussed, but even the visual observer is badly handicapped by the turbulence and dirtiness of our air. Even with the giant telescope on Palomar Mountain, which has a light-collecting mirror 200 inches in diameter, we cannot see far into the universe, while parochial problems such as the existence or nonexistence of the Martian canal system still remain to be solved.

Since the densest part of the atmosphere is that near sea level, large telescopes are generally erected at high altitudes. The loftiest of the great observatories is that of the Pic du Midi in the Pyrenees Mountains, but even at the Pic the altitude is only 10,000 feet—so that there is still a great deal of air above. Astronomers are forced to look through a sort of haze, and are much in the position of a man standing on Westminster Bridge trying to read the dial of Big Ben on a foggy night.

Above the atmosphere there would be no haze whatever. A comparatively small orbital telescope could show far more than the 200-inch can do from its site on Palomar, and incidentally the construction of large mirrors and lenses would be comparatively easy owing to their lack of weight. The worst problems to be faced in building the 200-inch were not optical, but mechanical; the mirror has to remain rigid to within a few millionths of an inch no matter how much the heavy instrument is shifted and tilted, and so long as we remain earth-based it seems that a larger telescope can hardly be built.

When the word "telescope" is mentioned, most people think automatically of an instrument which collects visible light by means of a lens or mirror. There is, however, another kind of instrument, the radio telescope, which is designed to focus not visible light but radiations of much longer wavelength. These "radio waves" are not blocked by interstellar dust and débris, so that they allow us to study regions of the universe which can never be seen in the normal way. Unfortunately radio telescopes, which are in the nature of aerials, have to be of great size—the largest yet

"Have you the time, old boy?"   "Haven't the foggiest"

built, at Jodrell Bank near Manchester in England, has a diameter of 250 feet—so that their use is restricted. Out in space these limitations would not apply.

As a physical laboratory, the space station would be of immense value. The best vacuum we can produce on earth is far inferior to that of the exosphere; nor can we simulate conditions of zero gravity. There are many branches of research which demand the use of very low pressures and total vacuum, and on the station it would also be possible to obtain a great range of temperature without the use of complex apparatus.

Even medicine would benefit directly. It has been stated that conditions of reduced or zero gravity would be beneficial to those who suffer from heart complaints, and in any case the study of human and animal reactions under such conditions will provide much information. At the moment it is sheer fantasy to talk about a "space hospital," but in two or three centuries from now the situation may be different.

There are many other aspects of the matter. It would, for instance, be possible to use satellites as radio and television relays, so that television coverage could be extended over the whole Earth (whether this would be a blessing or not is a moot point). But there is little to be gained from going into further details as yet. It is at least clear that the satellite will be well worth building.

However, the satellite will be valuable not only because of itself. It will provide us with a means of reaching the Moon—and this brings us at last to the question of true interplanetary travel.

WORLD WIDE TELEVISION

and possible effects on global culture.

CHAPTER 11

Into Space

WHEN the subject of interplanetary flight is brought up, one thinks instinctively of Mars and Venus. Mars, in particular, is an inviting world inasmuch as it has a tolerably thick atmosphere and seems to possess a good deal of vegetation. But before we can reach out for the planets, we must conquer the Moon, which is much less welcoming in itself but is comparatively near at hand.

The distance to the Moon is rather less than a quarter of a million miles, which is equivalent to ten nonstop trips round the Earth's equator. Such a distance is not impossibly great, and, moreover, the Earth and Moon are companions in space; they keep together as they circle the Sun, so that it will not be necessary to wait on the Moon for months before conditions are suitable for a return journey.

The setting-up of a manned satellite will bring the Moon within reach, but even before then it is possible that unmanned missiles will be directed there. This idea goes back to Professor Goddard's classic *Method of Reaching Extreme Altitudes*, when he proposed to launch a small rocket carrying enough magnesium powder to cause a visible flash when it landed.* A study of the movements of this missile would be most helpful, and a successful flash-powder experiment might lead on to the dispatch of instrument-carrying vehicles capable of sending back positive information.

Professor Oberth considered that Goddard had under-estimated the amount of powder needed to produce an observable flash, and other writers have doubted whether the idea is workable at all, but on the whole it seems probable that some such attempt will be made soon. My personal forecast is that it will be done before 1966, and it may even take place during the International Geophysical Year, though this view is certainly optimistic. Nor would there be much difficulty in observing the flash from Earth.

Following the flash experiment and the instrument-bearing missile, the next stage in our attack on the Moon will probably be to send a projectile that can do a complete circuit of the lunar globe before returning to Earth. This idea, too, is old. Jules Verne used it in his famous story, when he related how a wandering minor planet pulled his heroes out of their calculated path and swung them into an orbit that carried them right round the Moon. The necessary calculations are difficult, but not impossible, and if the experiment is carried through it will answer one of the burning questions of modern astronomy: "What lies on the far side of the Moon?"

The Moon revolves round the Earth in a period of 27 days 7 hours 43 minutes, or approximately one month. It takes precisely the same time to spin once on its axis, so that a lunar "day" is also equal to 27 days 7 hours 43 minutes. This means that the Moon keeps the same hemisphere turned perpetually towards the Earth, the opposite hemisphere being permanently averted.

* The Russian scientist Pokrovsky has even suggested a rocket carrying an atom bomb!

The best way to understand this is to put a chair in the middle of the room and then to walk round it, making the chair represent the Earth while your head stands for the Moon. If you begin with your face turned to the chair, and walk round so that you keep the chair in view all the time, you will have made one complete rotation on your axis by the time you have completed one circuit. This is how the Moon behaves. There is no mystery about it, and the apparent coincidence is explained easily enough by tidal friction in past ages, but the effect is infuriating for astronomers who want to examine all the Moon's surface and not only part of it.

Actually the situation is not quite so bad as might be thought. The Moon spins on its axis at a constant rate, but it does not move steadily round the Earth. Its orbit is not perfectly circular, and when closest to the Earth it naturally moves fastest, in obedience to Kepler's laws of planetary motion. The axial spin and position in orbit thus become slightly "out of step" at certain periods each month, and the Moon appears to be slightly tipped, so that astronomers can peer some distance round alternate edges. There is a secondary tipping or "libration" because the Moon's orbit is inclined to ours. Altogether, four-sevenths of the whole surface can be examined, while the remaining three-sevenths remains invisible.

Although it seems certain that the hidden part of the Moon is very like the part we can see, there is no hope of finding out more so long as we are chained to the Earth. A circumlunar rocket could bring back a complete photographic record, and this is a real possibility, though it will not be easy to recover the films even if the projectile can be made to fall back into a satellite orbit not far above the top of the atmosphere.

Actual expeditions to the Moon are another matter altogether, and cannot be planned as yet. They would not, however, be prolonged. At the velocities which we anticipate, such a journey would take a mere five days. A further five days for the return and a certain period spent on the Moon itself would mean a total absence of only a week or two, and there would be no major problems with regard to the provision of food and drink. This is very different from the case of a trip to Mars, which could not be completed in less than two years.

The pioneer lunar expedition is unlikely to take place until the manned satellite is in orbit, principally because of fuel difficulties. It must be remembered that we have to carry not only enough fuel to break free from the Earth, but enough to break free from the Moon again on the return trip—unless we are prepared to stay there indefinitely. (The hero of Jules Verne's story had a delightfully simple answer to the question of how he would come back: he merely said "I shall not come back.") Fortunately the return journey will be easier than the outward, owing to the lesser pull of the Moon.

The Moon has a mass of only 1/81 of that of the Earth, and escape velocity is 1½ miles per second instead of 7. This means that the blast-off from the lunar surface can be a comparatively mild affair, particularly in view of the virtual airlessness. Even with our present rockets a velocity of 1½ miles a second is well within our powers.

Just as it is still too early to decide upon a definite pattern for the manned satellite, we must admit that it would be premature to lay down hard and fast designs for a space ship. It seems likely that the lunar craft will be assembled out beyond the atmosphere, so that it will never have to move in dense air; wings will be superfluous, and instead of being a sleek, streamlined vessel shaped like a bullet it will more probably be a sphere fitted with retractable legs. Further speculations are rather pointless.

Let us assume that the lunar ship is to blast away from the

manned satellite, using normal liquid-fuel motors of the type with which we are familiar. Since the satellite is already moving round the Earth at orbital velocity (five miles per second) all that the lunar ship need do is to increase its speed from orbital to near actual escape velocity, and its own motors need provide less than an additional two miles per second.

Acceleration, giving the occupants the impression of normal Earth gravity, would last only for six to seven minutes. Then the motors would cut out and the craft would be in free fall, but in a new orbit—one which would take it to the Moon.

Four days later the ship would have approached to a distance of 24,000 miles from the Moon, at which point the lunar pull on it would be equal to the terrestrial. Jules Verne made much play of this "neutral point," when he mistakenly stated that the men inside his projectile became weightless only when they reached the neutral point, whereas in fact they would have been under conditions of zero gravity ever since leaving the Earth. The so-called neutral point is of no importance whatsoever, and in any case it should be remembered that in view of the powerful pull of the Sun the point is "neutral" only in the loosest sense of the word.

Five days after leaving the satellite, the rocket would arrive in the immediate vicinity of the Moon. If unchecked, it would hit the surface at 5,200 m.p.h., which would prove disastrous to both rocket and crew. Air braking by any form of parachute is out of the question on a world that is almost without atmosphere, and rocket braking would have to be used.

This means that the craft would be turned so that its exhaust pointed straight to the Moon. The motors would then be brought into play, firing against the direction of motion and slowing the rocket down. The landing maneuver would thus be the exact reverse of blast-off, and the final impact would be gentle enough to be borne by the shock-absorbing legs.

All this sounds delightfully easy, but in fact it is nothing of the kind. The slightest error in the original calculations would lead to disaster in view of the lack of fuel reserve, and the landing itself would be a most hazardous business, since a violent drop would damage the craft so that it would be unable to blast off again. Subsidiary difficulties, such as making the rocket completely airtight and allowing for a sufficient oxygen supply for the crew, do not concern us yet; but they will certainly concern the men who have the task of planning the details of the first expedition. There is no point in minimizing the dangers.

However, several of the "bogies" which have been produced to disprove the whole interplanetary idea have turned out to be false alarms. Meteoric bombardment is one. The tiny micrometeorites are too small to do much harm, and a suitable outer bumper could deal with them, whereas the larger meteors are so rare that the chances of being hit by one during an Earth-Moon voyage are negligible. Ultra-violet radiation from the Sun can be screened, and on the whole it seems that long exposure to cosmic rays will not be harmful, though on this latter point a certain amount of doubt must remain.

Although we cannot blast away from the Earth's surface and make straight for the Moon, the converse is not true, owing to the low lunar gravity and the lack of air resistance. Eventually the ship would return to the orbit of the manned satellite, and the major part of the expedition would be at an end. There would still be the problem of traveling back from the satellite to the Earth itself, and oddly enough this would be even riskier than landing on the Moon.

The wingless lunar craft will be quite unsuitable for movement within an atmosphere, so that the crew will transfer to a ferry rocket. The exhausts will then be turned against the direction of motion, and power applied, so that the rocket will slow down in orbit and will move away from the manned satellite. It will spiral downwards until it enters the resisting air, and the most dangerous part of the whole undertaking will begin. Should the rocket move too quickly, it will become so hot by friction that it will turn into a shooting-star.

This point has not been overlooked by von Braun. On his theory, the rocket will enter the atmosphere in such an attitude that the wings will hold it down instead of helping it to rise. At once the temperature will increase, and friction against the air particles will make the ship so hot that its outer hull will glow bright red. This will be the worst period. Should the heat become too great, the hull will melt; the pilot will have to keep just within the atmosphere, where the air is too thin to cause much resistance, losing speed every second and balancing velocity against temperature. As the speed drops, he can risk venturing into deeper and denser regions. At last he will be moving slowly enough to turn the craft into a normal attitude, and it can then be handled in the same way as an aircraft, making its final landing in the usual manner.

Another proposed scheme is to allow the ship to graze the uppermost layers of air, losing a little velocity in the process before it shoots back into space on the far side of the Earth to cool off. It will then turn and graze the air again, so shedding more of the surplus velocity before returning to the comparative safety of space. After several such grazes, each one deeper than the last, the velocity will be reduced sufficiently to enable the craft to enter the denser atmosphere without fear of turning into a meteor.

Such a procedure is at least based on sound scientific principles. Whether it can actually be followed or not remains to be seen, but if the landing problem cannot be overcome we must abandon not only lunar voyages but also manned satellites.

Once again, the unmanned satellites hold the key to the whole situation. It is logical to suppose that as soon as several small vehicles have been set up, an attempt will be made to recover one of them by remote control. Experiments of such a nature are not likely to be long delayed, and we await them with impatience.

Whichever way we turn, we come back in the long run to the unmanned earth satellite, which alone can tell us whether the dreams of men like Oberth and von Braun are fantastic or not. It is therefore not illogical to claim that the present satellite program is the first step to the Moon.

CHAPTER 12

The Moon

LONG AGO before the invention of the telescope, it was believed that the Moon must be inhabited. This idea persisted until comparatively recent times, and even Sir William Herschel, who was the greatest astronomer of the late eighteenth and early nineteenth centuries and who served as the first President of the Royal Astronomical Society, considered the habitability of the Moon "an absolute certainty." It seemed therefore that the main problem was how to get there, and not how to survive when the journey had been accomplished.

Unfortunately, it has since been proved beyond all doubt that the Moon is uninhabited and uninhabitable. It is a most hostile world from our point of view, and problems of survival will be as pressing as those of the voyage itself.

We plan to go to the Moon; if our satellite programs are carried through satisfactorily, it is even possible that an attempt may be made during the present century, though to make any definite forecasts would be unwise. (My personal guess at A.D. 2000 is probably made more in hope than in expectation.) Therefore it is essential for us to find out as much as we can about the Moon itself, and we must turn to pure astronomy.

The Moon is the favorite object of study for the amateur with a small or moderate telescope, because it is the one world close enough to be seen really well without the use of giant instruments. One's first glance at it through a telescope of any power never fails to cause a gasp of wonder. The Moon is obviously different from the Earth; there are no seas, forests, or ice fields, and the gray surface is covered with hundreds upon hundreds of the circular formations that have become known as "craters."

Much of the lunar surface is bright, but there are also vast areas of darker material. Formerly it was believed that the bright areas were land and the dark patches water; though for centuries now it has been realized that there is no water anywhere on the Moon, the dark patches still retain their old names. We thus find a Mare Crisium (Sea of Crises), an Oceanus Procellarum (Ocean of Storms) and even a Sinus Roris (Bay of Dews).

A waterless world would have its disadvantages, but absence of liquid alone would not make it hopelessly hostile. The real trouble about the Moon is its lack of air, and this is a natural consequence of the low escape velocity.

When the Earth began its career as an independent body, it seems to have had an atmosphere made up largely of the light gas hydrogen. All gas is composed of atoms and molecules, and these fly about at high speeds. The speeds are further increased by heat, and since the young Earth was very warm the particles of the primary atmosphere exceeded escape velocity, so that they leaked away into space and were lost forever. For a period, then, the Earth was virtually airless. After a while a second atmosphere was evolved from the gases expelled from below the crust, and this secondary mantle was unable to escape, partly because it was made up of heavier, slower-moving gases, and partly because the Earth had cooled down.

The early history of the Moon was probably similar, but its low escape velocity of only 1½ miles a second made it unable to retain even the secondary atmosphere. This too leaked away into space, and for millions of years now the Moon has been almost devoid of air. This means that it must also be virtually lifeless.

Up to now, we have to confess that we have no definite proof of the existence or nonexistence of a lunar atmosphere of any sort. The maximum density possible upon theoretical grounds is about 1/10,000 that of our own atmosphere, and in 1948 the Russian astronomer Y. N. Lipski announced the definite discovery of such an atmosphere; Lipski's results were supported by other workers, and it seemed that a mantle of this order certainly existed. Very recently, however, radioastronomy methods have been applied to the problem, chiefly by British workers, and the results are somewhat discouraging. Far from confirming Lipski's figure, the new researches seem to indicate that the lunar atmosphere has a density of less than 1/100,000 that of the earth's.

At first sight it might not appear important to decide between 1/10,000 and 1/100,000, since in neither case would the atmosphere be of the slightest use for breathing purposes, but actually the question is a vital one. Were the ground density as high as 1/10,000, the lunar atmosphere would still be an effective shield against meteoric bombardment. The density would fall off only slowly with increasing altitude, and at a height of 50 miles would be comparable with that at 50 miles above the Earth, which is the height at which most of our meteors burn out. On the other hand, a density of only 1/100,000 would mean that as a shield the atmosphere would be useless, and any permanent colony might have to be an underground one. However, definite proof either way is still lacking, and the whole question remains open.

It has been suggested that the Moon may be covered with a layer of dust many feet or even miles deep, and this would cause obvious complications. Fortunately the idea seems to be untenable; there may be an ashy layer, but it is not likely to be more than an inch deep, so that there will be no danger of a landing space craft falling into a kind of lunar quicksand.

The presence of ash is supported by other lines of research. The Moon's virtual lack of air means that during daylight the surface is fiercely heated, and on the lunar equator the maximum temperature rises to about that of boiling water. Now and then, however, the Moon passes into the shadow of the Earth; all direct sunlight is cut off, and the Moon is eclipsed. Direct measures show that the consequent fall in temperature is very rapid (during the 1939 eclipse, for instance, the temperature fell from +160 to −110 degrees Fahrenheit in only one hour). Ash is very poor at retaining heat, and would be expected to behave in this way. Moreover, investigations with radio waves have made it possible to measure the temperature a few feet below the outer surface, and this turns out to be remarkably uniform, showing that the ashy layer protects the Moon's interior from the tremendous temperature variations of the crust.

The presence of ash is not hard to explain. As we know, the Moon is pitted with circular walled formations which range from great plains well over 100 miles in diameter down to tiny pits at the very limit of visibility. It seems that these are basically volcanic, though formed in a different fashion from terrestrial craters such as Vesuvius. In past ages there must have been a great deal of igneous activity on the Moon, and a plentiful supply of volcanic ash is only to be expected, while there is bound to be a quantity of meteoric dust as well.

The Earth-facing portion of the Moon has been well charted. The latest and best chart, that of the British as-

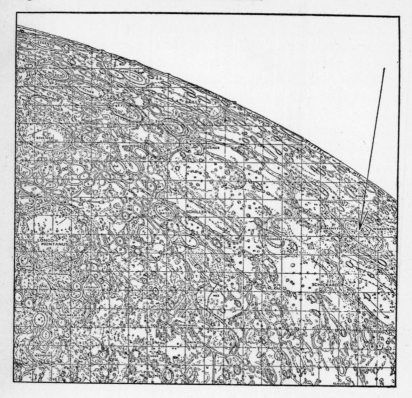

tronomer Dr. H. P. Wilkins, shows about 90,000 craters, and it is therefore possible to discuss the question of landing sites.

A glance at any lunar map or chart shows that the "seas" lie largely in the north and east, and these sea areas are to be favored on account of their relative smoothness. However, it is wrong to suppose that any part of the Moon is really level—despite the mirror-like smoothness of some areas as shown in photographs. A specific example of this may be given. One of the most interesting features of the Moon is the lava-filled crater Wargentin, which lies near the larger but more normal formation Schickard.* It is 55 miles across, and most drawings and photographs show the interior as completely smooth. In the detail map at top of page 130, arrow points to the crater Wargentin. (This map is a section from Dr. Wilkins' 300-inch chart. It is reproduced from *The Moon,* by H. P. Wilkins and Patrick Moore, copyright, 1955, by permission of The Macmillan Company.) In 1952, however, I made a detailed drawing of it with the 33-inch telescope at the Observatory at Meudon, the most powerful instrument in Europe, and was able to chart over fifty objects inside the crater, ranging from ridges to hollows, mounds, peaks and smaller crater pits. Greater power would doubtless have revealed still more detail.

It would be unwise to select a landing site too close to the lunar equator, owing to the great heat near the middle of the fortnight-long lunar "day." We must look for a relatively smooth area in a more temperate zone, where the maximum heat is naturally less fierce. The site selected by von Braun is the Sinus Roris, while Wilkins has pointed out that the Mare Crisium would be just as good. It would be premature to come to any definite decisions as yet, and research with the aid of the unmanned circumlunar rocket may shed new light on the problem, but at least there is no harm in making an intelligent guess.

The first lunar expeditions will be mere reconnaissances, but if all goes well there will come a time when a permanent base must be set up. There have been many published designs for such bases, the favored pattern being a large plastic dome kept inflated by the air pressure inside it, and fitted with an air-lock for entry and exit. This may or may not be a reasonable picture, and until we have carried out surveys from the actual surface we shall be unable to decide whether

* Lunar craters are generally named after famous scientists of the past and present. This system of nomenclature was introduced by the Italian astronomer Riccioli, over three centuries ago.

such a dome can in fact be built. The alternative is to construct an underground base, either by mining or by utilizing natural caves. This method would have the advantage of protecting the base from temperature extremes (the midnight temperature anywhere on the Moon is about that of liquid air), but it depends largely upon our finding suitable caves.

There are many problems connected with the Moon itself which cannot be solved from our distance of a quarter of a million miles. One of these is the question of how the craters came into being. One school of thought is that they were formed by intense meteoric bombardment in past ages. It is true that a plunging meteor might make a crater not unlike a lunar one, and we do know of several such impact craters on Earth; but the theory depends upon the crater distribution being random, which is emphatically not the case. A glance at any detailed map or photograph will show that the craters tend to "line up." From the vast walled enclosures down to the tiny pits, we observe that they are frequently found in well-defined chains and groups; when one crater breaks into another, the larger is invariably the sufferer; and there are many cases of mountains crowned by small, symmetrically-placed craterlets.*

No such arrangement could be produced by the fall of meteors, whereas it would be expected upon an igneous theory—since formations would tend to appear in certain specific areas and along lines of crustal weakness. However, there is no positive proof as yet. My own view is that the meteoric theory is untenable, but geological surveys from the surface will clear the matter up.

It should be added that other less rational theories have been put forward from time to time. Herr Weisberger, of

---

* Using very large telescopes, Dr. Wilkins and I have found more than sixty of these—far too many to be explained on the theory of mere chance hits by falling bodies.

Vienna, is convinced that there are no true mountains or craters on the Moon at all, and that the telescopic appearance is due to storms and cyclones in a dense lunar atmosphere; the Spanish engineer Sixto Ocampo has put forward the atomic bomb theory, according to which the craters are the result of a violent civil war among the Moon's inhabitants (!).

Another debatable question concerns certain dark patches on the Moon which appear to spread and develop as the Sun rises over them. Professor W. H. Pickering, an American astronomer who died in 1938, believed that these patches were due to primitive vegetation which existed by drawing upon tenuous gases sent out by cracks in the ground. It is true that certain craters do occasionally show a "misty" appearance, indicating slight emission, but recent work seems to show that even primitive vegetation is improbable. However, it remains an intriguing possibility, and only interplanetary research can prove or disprove it.

Questions of this kind would in themselves suffice to make a lunar voyage worth while, but there are many additional reasons for attempting it. Consider, for instance, the advantages of a lunar observatory. Under conditions of low gravity and virtual vacuum, visual and radio telescopes of almost unlimited power could be built, and there would be no blocking-out of radiation such as occurs on Earth. Our knowledge of the universe, from nearby planets to distant galaxies, would increase a thousandfold. Physical, chemical, biological and medical laboratories would be of equal benefit to their respective sciences, a fact so obvious that it needs no elaboration.

Most important of all, the journey to the Moon will show us whether or not we have any hope of traveling to the more earthlike worlds of Mars and Venus. At the moment we simply do not know; we may have overlooked some fundamental difficulty that will wreck all our grandiose theories and plans, and it is as well to be cautious. If, however, we do manage to reach the Moon during the twenty-first century, it is not unreasonable to assume that the first Martian voyage will follow in the twenty-second.

CHAPTER 13

Future Developments

EVEN though we are still at the very beginning of practical research, it is possible that the Moon may be reached during the lifetimes of some of those who fought in the Second World War. We cannot be at all certain, but the chance exists. On the other hand, it is highly unlikely that any of the pioneer workers will survive for long enough to see the initial trips to the nearer planets, Mars and Venus. Here we must reckon not in thousands but in millions of miles; unless we can develop some new fuel, the journeys will take months; and associated "minor" problems are enormously increased.

Sir Harold Spencer Jones has stated that he does not believe that travel to Mars or Venus will ever be possible. Whether he is right or wrong remains to be seen, and until we have made an attack on the Moon we shall not know, but we must realize that our present knowledge is hopelessly inadequate. We can, of course, discuss the project, as will be done in the present chapter, but we must not forget that we have entered the realm of pure speculation. Within a

year or two, the artificial satellite will be fact—but the trip
to Mars will still be far away.

Mars is farther from the Sun than we are, and has an
average distance of 141½ million miles as compared with
our 93 million; Venus is closer in, at an average distance of
67 million miles. This means that the minimum distances
from Earth are 35 and 24 million miles respectively, so that
Venus is the nearer of the two. Also, very close approaches

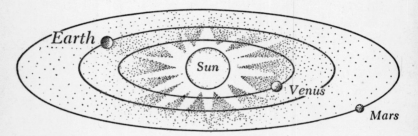

Mars is farther away from the Sun than we are, Venus is closer.

of Mars are rare, one of the best of our own century being
that of September 1956.

Unfortunately it is not possible for a rocket to take off
from the Moon or the manned satellite and race straight
across space to Mars, covering a mere 35 million miles in
the process. Theoretically this could be done with sufficient
power reserve, but so long as we are limited to our weak
liquid fuels we must be as economical as possible. Most of
the flight must be done in free fall, without constant application of power, and this involves a much longer journey.

Let us first consider the case of Mars. Since the Red World
is further from the Sun than we are, it moves more slowly
in its orbit—15 miles a second, instead of 18½. Suppose the
Earth could be made to speed up in its orbit? It would no
longer keep to its present path; it would draw slowly outwards, moving in an ellipse and slowing down as its dis-

tance from the Sun increased. We certainly cannot speed up the Earth, but there is a close analogy with what will be done in the case of a rocket bound for Mars.

In the illustration of the transfer orbit for Mars, E stands for the Earth and M for Mars. The rocket voyage will start by increasing the speed of the space ship relative to that of the Earth, when it will, of course, begin to move outwards along the second line or "transfer orbit," without any further application of power being necessary after the initial burst. If the calculations are sufficiently accurate, Mars and the rocket will then meet at the point M^1, so that a landing will be possible. Clearly the total distance traveled is more than 35 million miles, but the fuel expenditure is much less than for a direct journey by the shortest route. Nearly all the voyage will take place in free fall. It will take nine months, and there will be a prolonged stay upon Mars itself before the two planets are suitably placed for the return journey, so that the total absence will amount to at least two and a half years.

In the case of Venus, the rocket must be slowed down relative to the Earth. It will then move sunwards, and will meet Venus at the point V. Here the journey will be of only five months' duration, but the waiting period of Venus will be somewhat longer.

This sounds straightforward enough, but the complications are numerous enough to be terrifying. For one thing, there would be great difficulty in making the calculations to the required degree of accuracy, and if the rocket strayed from its predicted path there would be no hope for the unlucky occupants. In addition, problems such as food and water storage and oxygen supply, which are not too grave when we are dealing with the lunar project, will undoubtedly tax human ingenuity. The meteor danger is increased, and so is the effect of long exposure to ultraviolet and cosmic radiation, to say nothing of the unpleasant results of long-con-

tinued zero gravity (even if the space craft is rotated in
the manner of von Braun's "wheel"). Von Braun himself
considers that the first Martian expedition will comprise an
entire fleet of space craft, but though this sounds reasonable
enough it does not help us much in solving the fundamental
problems.

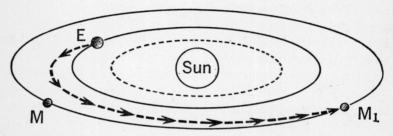

Transfer orbit to Mars carries rocket "outward," away from Sun.

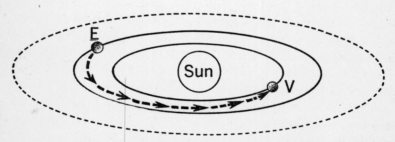

Transfer orbit to Venus. Rocket slows down and moves sunward.

Against this must be set the fact that Mars as a world is a
great improvement upon the Moon. There is an atmosphere,
there is a little water, and there is almost certainly extensive
vegetation. Nor is the temperature unbearable; a hot sum-
mer's day on the Martian equator may send the thermometer
up to over 80 degrees Fahrenheit, and although the nights

are bitterly cold they could be endured. Only in one respect is Mars hostile: the atmosphere, so far as we are concerned, is unbreathable. This point is important enough to be discussed in rather more detail.

Mars has only half the diameter and one-tenth the mass of the Earth, so that the escape velocity is lower (three miles a second). We would therefore expect a thinner atmosphere, though not a virtual vacuum as on the Moon, and this has been confirmed by practical research. The surface pressure is low, though great enough to prevent the blood-boiling danger, and is about equal to that at 55,000 feet above the Earth. This means that even if composed of pure oxygen, it could not be used by our lungs. However, it is not made up of oxygen; the amount of free oxygen is in fact very small, though the presence of polar ice and snow shows that a little must exist.

Many attempts have been made to analyze the atmosphere. The only positive result has been the detection of some carbon dioxide, and we can also assume that there is a little of the rare gas argon, but theoretical investigations show that the mantle is made up mainly of nitrogen. Nitrogen makes up 78 per cent of our own air, and is, of course, harmless, so that it is a fair comment to say that the Martian air resembles that of the Earth "with the oxygen taken out." At least it is not poisonous or corrosive, and it will form an efficient meteor screen.

Clouds can also be seen when Mars is favorably placed for observation. They are not, however, similar to our terrestrial clouds, and rainfall is certainly unknown.* The high-altitude clouds may well be made up of ice-crystals, thus

---

* In the recent film "Conquest of Space," advertised as being based on the book of the same name written by Willy Ley and illustrated by Chesley Bonestell, the Martian travelers arrived on a world where the sky was bright blue and contained Earthlike clouds; later on they even encountered a violent snowstorm. It is a great pity that such films are not made in accordance with known scientific facts.

resembling cirrus, while the lower "yellow clouds" are better explained as being dust storms.

Mars is not a great deal larger than the Moon, and is always more than a hundred times as distant, so that its surface is not known nearly so well. In a telescope, it appears as a reddish-ocher disk with bright white polar caps and dark patches nearer the equator. The caps have been shown to consist of a thin layer of icy or snowy material, while it

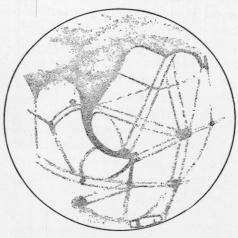

Mars as seen by Schiaparelli in 1888, showing so-called "canals."

can be assumed that the dark areas are due to lowly vegetation of the lichen or moss variety, though definite proof of this is still lacking. The ocher areas are often called "deserts," but are not sandy; they are probably deserts of dust, colored by minerals such as felsite or limonite. At any rate, the surface is solid enough, and no difficulties will be experienced on that score.

Mars has always been thought of as the one planet where intelligent life might exist, and forty years ago it was commonly believed that definite signs of activity had been de-

tected there. As long ago as 1877, the Italian observer
Schiaparelli drew attention to numerous long, straight, artificial-looking lines stretching across the deserts, connecting
the dark areas and forming a planet-wide network. These
"canals" were intensively studied by Professor Percival
Lowell, who constructed an observatory in Arizona specially
for the purpose, and it was stated that they were built by
Martian engineers to convey water from the icy poles down
to the arid temperate and equatorial regions.

Unfortunately, it is now known that the polar caps are
very thin. Even if all the water in them could be released at
once, it would fill only a moderate lake judged by our standards. Moreover, there are grave doubts as to whether the
canals exist at all in the form shown by Lowell and Schiaparelli; they are extremely delicate, too delicate to be photo-
graphed properly, and the human eye is very easily deceived
when straining to catch details near the limit of visibility.
The tendency is to join up disconnected spots and streaks
into sharp, artificial-looking lines.

The canals consist more probably of lowly vegetation,
and are not artificial waterways. It is still uncertain why
they extend for great distances in a semi-regular fashion, but
there can be little doubt that they are natural phenomena.
All lines of research indicate that Mars is not suitable for the
existence of advanced beings, and the intelligent Martians
so beloved by the story-tellers must be relegated to the world
of myth.

This particular question was settled some time ago, but in
recent years it has been reopened by the "flying saucer" craze
which has swept across America and Europe since 1947.
Various unidentified objects seen in the sky were held to
be space ships coming from Mars and Venus, and in 1952
landings were reported. One was said to take place in Cali-
fornia (though observers on Palomar Mountain did not appear to witness anything unusual!), and subsequently a

SPACE MEN are getting better looking...

Inhabitant of extragalactic realms

Bat men on the Moon

One of the "First Men on the Moon" by H. G. Wells

Allingham's Martian (out-of-focus drawing from out-of-focus photograph)

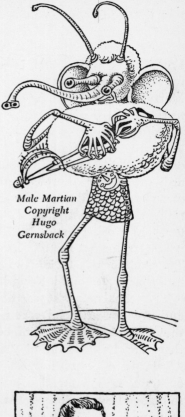

Male Martian Copyright Hugo Gernsback

Brother Bocco from Venus

Serious visualizations of male inhabitants from other worlds. There is a growing belief that they look just like you and me.

but the WOMEN have always been...

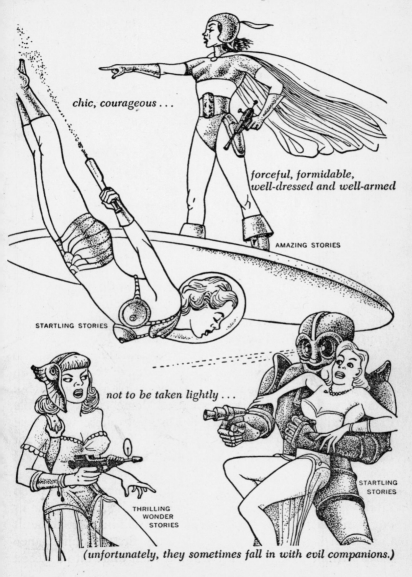

chic, courageous...

forceful, formidable, well-dressed and well-armed

AMAZING STORIES

STARTLING STORIES

not to be taken lightly...

THRILLING WONDER STORIES

STARTLING STORIES

(unfortunately, they sometimes fall in with evil companions.)

Scottish saucer was described in the famous book *Flying Saucer from Mars,* by Cedric Allingham. Allingham gave a detailed description of his conversation with a Martian who landed near Lossiemouth, and went so far as to produce a photograph of his interesting visitor. He did not, however, consider that the space man was identical with the Loch Ness Monster!

It is true that "flying saucers" do exist, inasmuch as many unidentified objects are reported each year; but almost all can be attributed to phenomena such as clouds, birds, ice crystals, high-altitude dust, and terrestrial aircraft. They are not interplanetary, and are thus no concern of the astronomer.

If and when a journey to Mars is attempted, it will not start from the surface of the Earth. It may do so from the Moon, but more probably from the manned satellite, since the "deep-space ship" will be incapable of traveling through an atmosphere. Fortunately we need not go to the trouble of building a manned satellite to orbit Mars. The Red World has two perfect space stations of its own in the shape of the two moonlets, Phobos and Deimos. The journey will thus take place in three stages—Earth to space station, space station to Deimos (or Phobos), and Deimos to Mars itself.

The Martian base will have to be constructed during the first voyage, since several months will have to be spent on the planet. At the moment we cannot even begin to tell what it will look like. A pressurized dome is a reasonable guess, and the comparatively dense atmosphere will make things much easier than on the Moon—it will certainly not be necessary to go underground—but further speculation is premature.

Venus presents us with different problems. There is no satellite; and since the escape velocity is almost the same as our own, blast-off on the return journey will be more difficult than from Mars. It is unlikely that the first reconnaissance parties will land at all. They will put their craft into a closed orbit above the planet, and do their best to find out whether actual exploration is or is not possible.

The trouble about Venus is that the opaque atmosphere prevents our seeing the true surface. The telescopic appearance is that of a bright and almost featureless disk, totally devoid of the permanent markings so characteristic of Mars, and infrared techniques are of no help. Vague shadings can be seen, but must be due to phenomena in the upper atmosphere of the planet; they drift and change from day to day, so that any attempt to draw up a map of Venus is doomed to failure.

We therefore know almost nothing about the surface conditions. Analysis of the atmosphere has revealed an abundance of the heavy, irrespirable gas carbon dioxide, and since this tends to produce a "greenhouse effect," shutting in the solar heat, it is inferred that the ground must be extremely hot. This has been confirmed by a recent announcement by radio astronomers from the Naval Research Laboratory in Washington, D.C. From a study of radio signals picked up by the Laboratory's radio telescope, they have calculated that Venus is hotter than boiling water (212° F). These results are, of course, tentative; radio astronomy is a young science. But Venus is likely to be super-tropical.

Until recently it was thought that Venus must be a howling desert, totally devoid of moisture and with gale-force winds sweeping constantly through the fuming atmosphere, but a new theory put forward by the American astronomers Drs. Whipple and Menzel seems to indicate that the planet is covered with a carbon-impregnated ocean. At the moment we have to confess that our ignorance is almost complete, and although Venus is the closest of the major planets it is the world about which we know least.

One definite fact is that the atmosphere is unbreathable. It is true that our analysis is limited to the uppermost layers, but all the evidence favors an "air" totally lacking free oxygen, so that for respiration it will be useless. We do not even know the length of Venus' "day." It is impossible to decide whether we shall ever be able to land there, but at any rate the planet is not likely to give us a friendly welcome.

The other planets of the Solar System are even less inviting. Mercury, which never approaches much within fifty million miles of us, is a curious and almost airless little world. It keeps the same face permanently towards the Sun, much as the Moon behaves with respect to the Earth, and the eternally sunlit face must have a maximum temperature of over +700 degrees Fahrenheit, while the region of constant night is bitterly chill. There is a zone between these two regions

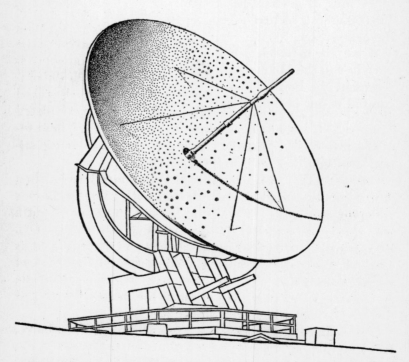

Fifty foot radio telescope of the Naval Research Laboratory at Washington

where the Sun would seem to rise and set, but generally speaking, Mercury is so hostile that it will probably never be visited.

The giant planets beyond the orbit of Mars have temperatures ranging from —200 degrees Fahrenheit (Jupiter) down to —360 degrees (Neptune), and their surfaces are not solid, so that landing on them is quite out of the question. Some of their larger satellites may be reached eventually—Titan, the sixth moon of Saturn, is larger than Mercury and even has a methane atmosphere—but certainly not for hundreds or even thousands of years. And interstellar flight, or travel to the hypothetical Solar Systems of other suns, is a scientific absurdity. Even light, moving at 186,000 miles a second, takes over four years to reach us from the nearest star.

If we are to reach other worlds, then, we must confine ourselves to the Moon, Mars and perhaps Venus. These three represent the limit of our ambitions—at least so far as we can tell in our present stage of scientific development.

CHAPTER 14

Summing Up

If ALL goes well, the next two or three years will see the beginning of the greatest experiment ever undertaken by man: the invasion of space. Yet we must always remember that the primary object of the satellite program is to explore the upper reaches of the atmosphere, and that true interplanetary flights are not possible yet. Before we can reach out for other worlds, we must learn as much as we can about our own.

On the other hand, space flight is no longer a dream. It is based upon something a great deal more solid than pure speculation, and if we continue to progress at our present rate we may hope for great things.

If we could indeed establish a manned satellite, we would accomplish far more than perhaps we know. Up to the present time the races of Earth have been in unceasing conflict, and technical progress during the past century has only made matters worse, but a venture of sufficient importance to all nations might lead to a lasting alliance. In landing upon the Moon, we could easily unite the Earth.

In short, there is every reason for continuing with inter-planetary research. At the very least, we are certain to learn more about the universe in which we live; even if we fail in our main object, we shall have the satisfaction of knowing that we have done our best.

All great experiments have humble beginnings. Aeronautics began with kites, with balloons, and with the clumsy machines developed by the Wrights, yet within forty years of the first proper ascent in a powered craft we had learned enough to soar to heights of many miles. The parallel is obvious enough, and we cannot doubt that the launching of the unmanned satellite will be a prelude to a new phase in the story of mankind.

Bibliography

BUEDELER, W. *To Other Worlds*. Burke Publishing Co., 1954.

BURGESS, E. *Frontier to Space*. Macmillan, 1955. Chapman & Hall, 1955.

CLARKE, A. C. *Interplanetary Flight*. Harper & Bros., 1951.

CLARKE, A. C. *The Exploration of Space*. Temple Press, 1955.

CLEATOR, P. E. *Into Space*. Allen & Unwin, 1953.

DE VAUCOULEURS, G. *Physics of the Planet Mars*. Faber & Faber, 1954.

DORNBERGER, W. *V2*. Viking, 1954. Hurst & Blackett, 1955.

HABER, HEINZ. *Man in Space*. Bobbs-Merrill, 1953.

LEY, W. *Rockets, Missiles and Space Travel*. Viking, 1952. Chapman & Hall, 1952.

MENZEL, D. H. *Flying Saucers*. Harvard University Press, 1953.

MOORE, PATRICK. *Guide to Mars*. Muller, 1956.

MOORE, PATRICK. *Guide to the Moon*. Norton, 1953.

MOORE, PATRICK. *Guide to the Planets*. Norton, 1954.

MOORE, PATRICK. *Story of Man and the Stars*. Norton, 1955.

MOORE, PATRICK. *The Planet Venus*. Faber & Faber, 1956.

NEWELL, HOMER E., JR. *High Altitude Rocket Research*. Academic Press, New York, 1953.

PENDRAY, E. G. *The Coming Age of Rocket Power*. Harper & Bros., 1947.

RICHARDSON, R. E. *Exploring Mars*. 1954.

ROSEN, C. *The Viking Rocket Story*. Harper & Bros., 1955.

STØRMER, C. *The Polar Aurora*. Oxford University Press, 1955.

STRUGHOLD, H. *The Green and Red Planet*. University of New Mexico Press, 1953.

VAETH, J. GORDON. *200 Miles Up*. Ronald Press, 1955.

WILLIAMS, B., and EPSTEIN, S. *The Rocket Pioneers*. Julian Messner, 1955.

Since the publication in 1936 of the first good popular work to appear in English, P. E. Cleator's *Rockets through Space,* many hundreds of books dealing with space flight have been written. It is naturally impossible to do more than mention a few, and in the short list above emphasis has been laid upon works which are not too highly speculative in character.

Index